Lessons from Grenfell 1

As a consequence of the Grenfell Tower fire, a building safety revolution is underway for construction and property professionals. This book analyses prior significant building fires and explains the new building safety regime including the Building Safety Act 2022 and the Building Safety Regulator. The aim is to provide an explanation of the Building Safety Regime. To that end, coverage includes:

- The Grenfell Tower fire: the Hackitt Review and Public Inquiry
- Remediation of existing buildings
- Legal Framework: the Fire Safety Act 2021 and Building Safety Act 2022
- Building Regulations: Part B Revisions and the Combustible Material Ban
- The Building Safety Regulator
- Guidance and Consultations

Change has arrived for construction and property professionals in the wake of the Grenfell Tower fire. This book is for readers who have responsibilities in the Built Environment or Real Estate to take the first steps towards implementation and compliance with the new regime.

Jennifer Charlson is Modern Methods of Construction Programme Manager at the Infrastructure and Projects Authority (IPA), UK.

Nenpin Dimka is an architect studying for a PhD in Architecture and Built Environment at the University of Wolverhampton, UK.

Lessons from Grenfell Tower
The New Building Safety Regime

Jennifer Charlson
Nenpin Dimka

Routledge
Taylor & Francis Group

LONDON AND NEW YORK

Designed cover image: © Shutterstock

First published 2024
by Routledge
4 Park Square, Milton Park, Abingdon, Oxon OX14 4RN

and by Routledge
605 Third Avenue, New York, NY 10158

Routledge is an imprint of the Taylor & Francis Group, an informa business

© 2024 Jennifer Charlson and Nenpin Dimka

British Library Cataloguing-in-Publication Data
A catalogue record for this book is available from the British Library

Library of Congress Cataloging-in-Publication Data
Names: Charlson, Jennifer, author. | Dimka, Nenpin, author.
Title: Lessons from Grenfell Tower : the new building safety regime /
Jennifer Charlson and Nenpin Dimka.
Description: Milton Park, Abingdon, Oxon ; New York, NY : Routledge, 2023.|
Includes bibliographical references and index.
Identifiers: LCCN 2023011731 | ISBN 9781032413143 (hbk) |
ISBN 9781032390024 (pbk) | ISBN 9781003357452 (ebk)
Subjects: LCSH: Grenfell Tower (London, England)—Fire, 2017. | Building,
Fireproof—Great Britain. | Building—Standards—Great Britain. |
Construction industry—Safety regulations—Great Britain.
Classification: LCC TH9449.L6 C48 2023 | DDC 693.8/20941—dc23/
eng/20230330
LC record available at https://lccn.loc.gov/2023011731

ISBN: 978-1-032-41314-3 (hbk)
ISBN: 978-1-032-39002-4 (pbk)
ISBN: 978-1-003-35745-2 (ebk)

DOI: 10.1201/9781003357452

Typeset in Times New Roman
by codeMantra

Contents

Chronology

2015	Grenfell Tower refurbishment construction commenced
Jan 2016	Grenfell Tower – Grenfell Action Group expressed concern that people might be trapped in the building in the event of a fire, emphasising the building's single entrance and exit, along with the corridors that had accumulated rubbish
June 2016	Grenfell Tower – 40 significant issues with fire safety were identified by an independent assessor
2016	Grenfell Tower refurbishment completed
Nov 2016	Grenfell Tower – a fire deficiency notice was issued by the London Fire and Emergency Planning Authority to KCTMO containing a list of actions, including concerns with fire doors and firefighters' lift controls
May 2017	Grenfell Tower – deadline for KCTMO to comply with the fire deficiency notice
2016–2017	Grenfell Tower gas supply works
14 June 2017	Grenfell Tower fire
Aug 2017	Grenfell Tower Public Inquiry, chaired by Sir Martin Moore-Bick, was set up
Sept 2017	Government commissioned Dame Judith Hackitt to review the Building Regulations and Fire Safety
Dec 2017	Interim Hackitt Report published
May 2018	Final Hackitt Report published
May 2018	Grenfell Tower Public Inquiry Phase 1 hearings began
May 2018	£400 million Social Sector ACM Cladding Remediation Fund
Dec 2018	The Building (Amendment) Regulations 2018 came into force
Dec 2018	Grenfell Tower Public Inquiry Phase 1 hearings concluded
May 2019	£200 million Private Sector ACM Cladding Remediation Fund
Oct 2019	The Grenfell Tower Public Inquiry Chairman published his Phase 1 Report
Jan 2020	Grenfell Tower Public Inquiry Phase 2 hearings began
March 2020	£1 billion Building Safety Fund
Dec 2020	£30 million Waking Watch Relief Fund
Feb 2021	Five point plan to end to unsafe cladding
Feb 2021	£3.5 billion added to the Building Safety Fund (total £4.5 billion)
April 2021	Fire Safety Act 2021 received Royal Assent
July 2021	Independent Expert Statement on Building Safety in medium and lower rise blocks of flats published. Government responded that it would support and act on the five recommendations
August 2021	The Town and Country Planning (Development Management Procedure and Section 62A Applications) (England) (Amendment) Order 2021 relevant provisions came into force i.e. Planning Gateway 1
Sept 2021	£5 million addition to the Waking Watch Relief Fund (total £35 million)
Jan 2022	£27 million Waking Watch Replacement Fund

Jan 2022	New plan to protect leaseholders and make industry pay for the cladding crisis
Jan 2022	Letter from the Secretary of State to the residential property developer industry
Jan 2022	Government withdrew the Consolidated Advice Note
April 2022	Building Safety Levy announced
April 2022	Residential Property Developer Tax (RPDT) came into force
April 2022	Building Safety Act 2022 (BSA) received Royal Assent
May 2022	The Building Safety Act 2022 (Commencement No. 1, Transitional and Saving Provisions) Regulations 2022 were made
May 2022	Fire Safety Act 2021 came into force
June 2022	New limitation periods for Defective Premises Act 1972 claims
June 2022	Building Liability Orders came into force
June 2022	Under Sections 147 to 155 of the BSA, a damage claim can be brought against a manufacturer of construction products whose breaches of the Construction Products Regulations 1991 cause a building or dwelling to become unfit for habitation
June 2022	Remediation Order (s123 of the BSA) and the Remediation Contribution Order (s124 of the BSA) came into effect
June 2022	Leaseholder protections in the BSA came into force
June 2022	Building Safety Regulator was established under the Health and Safety Executive
June 2022	Amendments to the Architects Act 1997
June 2022	Letter from the Secretary of State to freeholders, building landlords, and managing agents
July 2022	The Construction Products (Amendment) Regulations 2022 came into force
July 2022	The Building Safety (Leaseholder Protections) (England) Regulations 2022 came into force
July 2022	The Building Safety (Leaseholder Protections) (Information etc.) (England) Regulations 2022 came into force
July 2022	Under Section 48 of the BSA, the requirements relating to insurance for approved inspectors were removed from the Building Act 1984
July 2022	The Building (Approved Inspectors etc.) (Amendment) (England) Regulations 2022 came into force
July 2022	£4.5 billion Building Safety Fund re-opened
July 2022	48 of the UK's major housebuilders had signed up to the government's Building Safety Pledge
July 2022	The Department for Levelling Up, Housing & Communities published two Building Safety consultations
July 2022	The Department for Levelling Up, Housing & Communities published a Residents' Voice consultation
August 2022	The Department for Levelling Up, Housing & Communities published the HSE Consultation: Building Safety Operational Standards Rules

August 2022	The Department for Levelling Up, Housing & Communities published the HSE Consultation: The Building Safety (Fees and Charges) Regulations 202[3] and charging scheme
August 2022	The Building Safety Act 2022 (Commencement No. 2) Regulations 2022 were made
Oct 2022	New Homes Ombudsman Service launched
Oct 2022	Social housing complainants can escalate a complaint directly to the Housing Ombudsman service
Oct 2022	The Health and Safety Executive Building Inspector Competence Framework (BICoF) consultation opened
Nov 2022	The Building Safety Act 2022 (Commencement No. 3 and Transitional Provision) Regulations 2022 were made
Nov 2022	Grenfell Tower Public Inquiry Phase 2 hearings concluded
Dec 2022	The Building etc. (Amendment) (England) Regulations 2022 came into force
Jan 2023	The Fire Safety (England) Regulations 2022 came into force
April 2023	Building Safety Regulator due to become operational

Legislation and cases

Statutes

An Act for rebuilding the City of London 1667
Architects Act 1997
Building Act 1984
Building Safety Act 2022
Building (Scotland) Act 2003
Defective Premises Act 1972
Fire Safety Act 2021
Inquiries Act 2005
Public Health Act 1875

Secondary legislation

Regulatory Reform (Fire Safety) Order 2005
The Building (Amendment) Regulations 2018
The Building (Approved Inspectors etc.) (Amendment) (England) Regulations 2022
The Building (Approved Inspectors etc.) Regulations 1985
The Building (Approved Inspectors etc.) Regulations 2010
The Building etc. (Amendment) (England) Regulations 2022
The Building (First Amendment) Regulations 1973
The Building (Prescribed Fees) Regulations 1980
The Building Regulations 1965
The Building Regulations 1972
The Building Regulations 1976
The Building Regulations 2000
The Building Regulations 2010
The Building Regulations (Amendment) (No. 2) Regulations 1999
The Building (Scotland) Regulations 2004
The Building (Third Amendment) Regulations 1975
The Building Safety Act 2022 (Commencement No. 1, Transitional and Saving Provisions) Regulations 2022

The Building Safety Act 2022 (Commencement No. 2) Regulations 2022
The Building Safety Act 2022 (Commencement No. 3 and Transitional Provision) Regulations 2022
The Building Safety (Leaseholder Protections) (England) Regulations 2022
The Building Safety (Leaseholder Protections) (Information etc.) (England) Regulations 2022
The Construction Products (Amendment) Regulations 2022
The Fire Safety (England) Regulations 2022
Town and Country Planning (Development Management Procedure and Section 62A Applications) (England) (Amendment) Order 2021

Cases

Bolam v Friern Hospital Management Committee [1957] 2 All ER 118
Martlet Homes Limited v Mulalley & Co. Limited [2022] EWHC 1813 (TCC).
Murphy v Brentwood District Council [1991] UKHL 2
Rendlesham Estates v Barr Ltd [2014] EWHC 3968 (TCC)
St James's Oncology SPC Limited v Lendlease Construction (Europe) Limited & Another [2022] EWHC 2504 (TCC)

Introduction

The historical backdrop to the Grenfell Tower fire is considered by analysis of the Summerland (1973), Knowsley Heights (1991), Garnock Court (1999), Harrow Court (2006) and Lakanal House (2009) fires. These fires exemplify several aspects considered as warning signs which could have prevented the scale of the Grenfell Tower disaster.

A fire which destroyed Grenfell Tower in June 2017 resulted in the death of 72 people. The government's response included appointing Dame Judith Hackitt to lead an independent review and setting up a public inquiry, chaired by Sir Martin Moore-Bick (a retired Lord Justice of Appeal), to examine the circumstances leading up to and surrounding the fire at Grenfell Tower.

Building a Safer Future – Independent Review of Building Regulations and Fire Safety ('the Hackitt Review'), published in May 2018, set out principles for a new regulatory framework. The Phase 1 Report of the public inquiry, published in October 2019, focused on the events that occurred during the night of the fire.

In the Queen's Speech in December 2019, the government announced that it intended to introduce a Building Safety Bill that would "*Put in place new and enhanced regulatory regimes for building safety and construction products, and ensure residents have a stronger voice in the system*". A Fire Safety Bill was also announced that would "*implement the relevant legislative recommendations of the Grenfell Tower Public Inquiry Phase 1 Report*".

The Fire Safety Act 2021, which commenced on 16 May 2022 and applies to England and Wales, amended the Regulatory Reform (Fire Safety) Order 2005.

The Building Safety Act 2022, which received Royal Assent on 28 April 2022, introduced new and enhanced regulatory regimes for building safety. The Housing Secretary Robert Jenrick described the reforms as "*the biggest change to our building safety regime for 40 years*". The construction and real estate industries will need to adapt to the extensive regulatory reform. Cultural change in the industries should be driven by significant new duties for buildings throughout their life cycle.

In accordance with the outline transition plan, a number of changes have been implemented with the bulk of the new provisions due to come into force 12 to 18 months after Royal Assent.

The Building Safety Act (BSA) 2022 created three new bodies to provide effective oversight of the new regime: the Building Safety Regulator, the National Regulator of Construction Products and the New Homes Ombudsman.

The Building Safety Regulator (BSR) was established under the Health and Safety Executive in June 2022 and is due to become operational in April 2023. The BSR has a duty to establish and maintain three committees: Residents' Panel, Industry Competence Committee and Building Advisory Committee.

The BSA included the introduction of a new regime of regulatory measures for high-rise residential and other in scope buildings. Between October 2023 and October 2028, all existing buildings will come into the scope of the regulations.

The BSR will regulate developments through a series of three gateways. Permission from the BSR will be required before a development can proceed through each gateway. Gateway 1, which governs the planning stage, is already in force. From October 2023, developers will also have to pass through gateway 2 prior to the start of building work and gateway 3 upon the works' completion.

Occupational phase building safety duties are shared between dutyholders. The Landlord is required to comply with the BSA and cooperate with other dutyholders. The Accountable Person will need to apply for a Building Assessment Certificate to verify that they are meeting their prescribed duties.

The BSA has inserted a new Part 2A 'Regulation of the Building Control Profession' into the Building Act 1984. Registration will open in October 2023 with the sections of the BSA related to registration coming into force in April 2024.

An overview of the building regulations is given with regulations and guidance distinguished. Amendments as a consequence of the Grenfell Tower fire, in particular to Approved Documents B, are detailed.

The leaseholder protections in the BSA are in force with new financial protections for leaseholders in buildings above 11 m or 5 storeys with historical safety defects. The BSA has extended existing rights under the Defective Premises Act 1972 and the Building Act 1984. Building liability, remediation and contribution orders are also in force.

The government established remediation, building safety, waking watch relief and waking watch replacement funds. The Residential Property Developer Tax then came into force, and a Building Safety Levy was announced.

Many of the UK's major housebuilders signed up to the government's Building Safety Pledge. The building safety programme has, on a monthly basis, released its data.

Building safety procurement and fire risk assessment and appraisal guidance have been published. To complete the new building safety regime, a number of consultations have been issued. The outcome of the consultations will inform the subsequent secondary legislation, which will bring the proposed changes into force.

The law is stated as the authors consider it to be as of 1 January 2023. Unless otherwise stated, the law in this book applies to England. Those in Scotland, Wales and Northern Ireland should check for differences which may be applicable in their regions.

The contents are not to be interpreted as legal or professional advice.

1   Background

Nenpin Dimka

1.1   Introduction

This chapter sets the scene of fires that have occurred in the buildings in the United Kingdom (UK), including high-rise residential buildings, as a historical backdrop and chain of events which have led up to and necessitated the new building safety regime. The premise is these historical events could have given sufficient insight to avert the disaster of the Grenfell Tower fire. Some of the lessons were ignored, and improvements in the construction industry can be established to be reactive. Finally, there is evidence to suggest despite some tragic events, there has always been an eventual drift back to focus on price over quality or safety.

Over the past half-century, the UK has experienced several fires in buildings. However, five key fires have been described as the fires that predicted the Grenfell fire disaster on the night of 17th June 2017.

Five events are considered to highlight the causes and key factors which contributed to the disaster experienced. Each event concludes with the steps taken in the aftermath of these events, including investigations and recommendations made and some key lessons.

The five fires revisited include the Summerland Disaster, Douglas, Isle Of Man (1973); Knowsley Heights Fire, Liverpool, England (1991); Garnock Court Fire, Irvine, Scotland (1999); Harrow Court Fire, Stevenage, England (2005); and Lakanal House Fire, London, England (2009).

1.2   Summerland 1973

1.2.1   Background

Forty-four years prior to Grenfell, a fire considered to be the deadliest since the Blitz in England – World War II, engulfed a building designed with the intent to provide the illusion of sunlight most days of the year for the function of entertaining up to 10,000 holidaymakers.

The Summerland leisure centre in Douglas on the Isle of Man was opened on 25 May 1971. It was a climate-controlled building covering 3.5 acres on the waterfront. Its design was expected to establish a new precedent in modern architecture

DOI: 10.1201/9781003357452-1

Figure 1.1 Summerland and the Aquadrome.

and revive British seaside tourism, which was dwindling in favour of group tours to the Mediterranean. This was to be achieved through the concept of Summerland as a weatherproof enclosure using what was considered, at the time, a highly innovative building material.

Its exteriors and interiors were designed by two different architects, as a consequence of financial decisions. This was later discovered to have been the cause of the building having significant potential fire hazards, including inadequate fire exits.

1.2.2   The events of the fire

On the night of 2 August 1973, a fire is thought to have started in a kiosk by a discarded match or stub, on the terrace, the kiosk then collapsed onto the east wall of the building's exterior.

The indoor holiday park had been wrapped with a material that was highly innovative at the time, a polymethylmethacrylate sheeting known as "Oroglas". It was manufactured by an American company and had not been used at the scale the designers of Summerland had committed to using on the building. The whole roof and most parts of the elevation were clad with Oroglas. This material was known to the manufacturers as being combustible and, when subject to temperatures well below the ignition point, would soften and fall out of its frame.

However, another substance, "Galbestos", a cheaper alternative to concrete or regular steel sheeting, was used on the building's east wall. Galbestos was rolled steel sheeting covered with asbestos felt, saturated with bitumen and then faced with a polyester resin coating.

1.2.3   Spread of fire

The external fire from the kiosk ignited the Galbestos combustible coating in seconds, owing to its steel core's high thermal conductivity, fumes were emitted from the wall's interior in minutes as the Galbestos was in flames.

Figure 1.2a Summerland's 10ft Oroglas Promenade Wall and the terrace where the fire started.

Figure 1.2b Summerland's 10ft Oroglas Promenade Wall.

Figure 1.3 The Galbestos wall at the eastern end of the complex.

When the fire entered into the void between the external Galbestos and the inner wall, which was made of "Decalin" – a combustible plastic-coated fibreboard, it grew temperatures suspected to be up to 1,000 °C. The fire breached the interior of the building at the ceiling level. By this time a significant portion of the interior wall had been burning for quite some time – as the fire went undetected for 20 minutes after it had begun. The fire spread, rapidly igniting the Oroglas promenade wall in seconds, and burning plastic began dribbling to lower levels.

Neither a fire alarm nor a warning was given, nor was an official evacuation order made except for the shouted instructions of a terrified speaker. Two of the main entrance doors and one fire exit were locked out of the very limited number of exits available in the building. People were advised not to panic, and 3000 people remained in the building. A toxic black smoke overwhelmed the people, and they lost their way. Children playing on the lower level were separated from the parents on the upper terraces. The fire engulfed the building in approximately 30 minutes, causing the death of 50 people, with 80 people seriously injured.

1.2.4   Response

A public inquiry ran from September 1973 to February 1974. It condemned the use of flammable materials in the building and the delay in evacuation. On its own, the kiosk fire would not have caused the disaster, but the material, particularly, Galbestos, was responsible for the scale of the disaster experienced.

The use of Oroglas was permitted based on waiver requested by the architect and granted by the Borough Engineer due to a series of failures to communicate. Consequently, By-law 39 of the Isle of Man was waived in order to allow the use of Oroglas, with the belief that it was non-combustible and in the event of a fire it would theoretically soften and fall out of its frames, allowing people to escape through the gridwork of the walls.

The Summerland Fire Commission report revealed the catastrophic outcome of the event was owed to the materials used. The combination of Galbestos and Decalin was also found to be a significant contributor to the spread of the fire during its early stages, in tandem with the open plan designs, insufficient staircases and exits, which were attributed to poor communication and limited research on the part of the architects and planners.

1.2.5   Outcome

Human error was cited as the cause of the disaster in the official report. Corners were found cut due to cost savings, and sprinklers were not installed. Changes to building regulations to improve fire safety were introduced, and in 1975 the House of Commons passed an amendment that strengthened regulations across the UK. External walls of large buildings were now mandated to always be fire-resistant. The inquiry found the "stay put" policy significantly impacted the evacuation.

The final report also called for the installation of sprinklers in all large buildings and recommended cladding of large buildings in non-flammable materials. The tighter Regulations meant the fire service would be involved to a much greater extent in ensuring adequate levels of public safety are maintained. By-laws were introduced to emphasise the need for barriers to prevent the vertical and horizontal spread of fire inside a building.

The changes to UK Building Regulations (known as the Summerland Amendments) were gradually introduced following the disaster. These new regulations were largely concerned with means of escape from a building and fire spread. The whole of Part E of the 1972 Building Regulations dealing with Structural Fire Precautions was amended by The Building (First Amendment) Regulations 1973, which came into force on 31st July 1974. In December 1975, further amendments followed in The Building (Third Amendment) Regulations 1975. This amendment specified that the external walls of public buildings must always be fire-resistant. The legislation also prevented flammable materials from being used for the lower levels of a building, where they would be in contact with the building's floors or could be reached by a human being. These walls must be non-combustible and fire-resistant throughout and use materials such as brick, stone and concrete. A guidance document was issued by the UK Home Office (Circular 32/1975) on 12th March 1975. The document stated it would be beneficial for the fire brigade to inspect leisure and holiday centres whilst the public is on the premises to ensure regulations, conditions of the licence and good practice are being observed.

1.3 Knowsley Heights 1991

1.3.1 Background

Eighteen years after the Summerland fire, Britain's first tower block cladding fire happened in Huyton, Merseyside. Knowsley Heights was a tower block considered a blight on the city and became part of a government-launched state action to improve living conditions in tower blocks which included an overclad scheme, a technique relatively new to public sector housing. The envisaged improvements were centred on the reduction of energy consumption and the appearance of the tower block.

Figure 1.4 Knowsley Heights in Merseyside.

The Knowsley Heights fire occurred in 1991 following the installation of the new cladding, which was later found to essentially be a flammable wrapper around the building. The 11-story block had 64 flats on either side of a central service core containing lifts and stairs. It was built in 1963 and, in 1988, was extensively refurbished. Earlier improvements included the enclosing of the open balconies.

The block also had a history of severe damp, which had been treated unsuccessfully with a bituminous compound. The 1988 scheme also involved the use of a Class 0 rainscreen cladding on aluminium support rails. Furthermore, the size of the windows had been reduced, and new double-glazed uPVC units had been installed.

1.3.2   The events of the fire

The fire started when rubbish was deliberately set alight outside of the tower block. The flames started at the bottom and spread through a 90 mm cavity between the wall and the newly insulated rain screen cladding. The spread of the fire caused extensive damage to the walls and windows, but the interior did not suffer damage.

The cladding started approximately 100 mm from ground level and extended up to the roof. The "Gunac" layer had been scored at intervals to allow moisture to move out of the building. The insulation used was 100 mm thick mineral wool fixed against the building with a 90 mm air gap to allow air movement behind the cladding. However, cavity barriers were not fitted, although this was permitted under the prevailing guidance where the cladding system was not combustible, this meant unrestricted airflow could not be ensured.

In addition, there were gaps created due to the difference in the size of the old and new windows, which were filled in with strand boards on wood studs. A coating of steel was applied to the window ledges, and a large cavity of about 0.5 m depth was created behind the cladding where the windows were in recessed areas of the building.

1.3.3   Spread of fire

On one elevation, all the cladding on the 11 stories was destroyed. In the cavity behind the newly installed rainscreen cladding, the fire spread vertically, melting the aluminium support as well as the strand boards and uPVC frames that enclose the window reveals. The size of the cavity contributed significantly to the spread of fire.

Several interior areas of the building were affected by the fire, including the access corridors on the ground, first and tenth floors. There was also damage caused by smoke and heat on other floors. On almost every floor, Georgian-wired glass between the access corridor and the central left lobby was cracked. No flats were affected by fire or smoke.

All residents were evacuated, and there was no loss of lives, primarily due to the fact that the fire occurred adjacent to an unoccupied area of the building, even though it was a common area.

1.3.4 Response

Based on the findings of the Building Research Establishment (BRE), the cladding around Knowsley Heights had a low combustibility risk. Additionally, it noted there were no firebreaks in the building. The cladding used in Knowsley Heights was deemed legal. New guidance was drawn up and effective from 1st June 1992, addressing the particular problem of cavity barriers in rain screen cladding.

1.3.5 Implication

In the past, regulations were mainly concerned with internal fire spreads spreading out of buildings and not the other way around, as was the case with Knowsley Heights. Guidance on cavity barriers was scrutinised following the fire spread through the whole vertical height of the building.

A formal requirement to ensure buildings met fire safety regulations was eliminated six years earlier when the government reduced building regulations from more than 300 pages to just 25 in a bid to reduce processes and compliance, which seemed unnecessary and delayed results.

A review from the Thatcher government called for an overhaul of fire policy due to the "significant financial burden" of the legislation. The review recognised that removing control would "lead to recurrence, albeit infrequently, of multiple fatality fires". Nonetheless, it advocated reductions in fire cover "which would not result in an unacceptable increase in loss of property or casualties".

To aid compliance with new laws by the construction industry, a guidance document was produced to support the Building Regulations – called the Approved Document B (ADB). As a guidance document, it outlined the products that could be used in construction generally, for instance, cladding.

1.3.6 Outcome

ADB was updated following the fire to specify the types of material permitted, but cladding was not required to be fire resistant. The recommendations were the use of cavity masonry cladding on the ground floor to resist impact and fire, as was common practice in very tall blocks found around the country. But Knowsley Heights had been an exception because it had living accommodations on the ground floor, and the cladding was fitted up until within 100 mm of ground level.

Where Class 0 is required, BRE suggested that it should be Class 0 on both sides of the cladding exposed to air. However, two critical factors were at play in this fire: the exposure of both sides of the cladding to the fire and the melting of the aluminium rails due to high temperatures.

1.4   Garnock Court 1999

1.4.1 Background

The Garnock Court fire was a fire that took place on 11 June 1999 in a 14-storey block of flats in Irvine, Scotland. The block was one of five blocks owned by the

Figure 1.5a Damaged South Elevation of Garnock Court.

Figure 1.5b Detail of window below fire damage.

North Ayrshire Council and part of a refurbishment and reinstatement scheme. For decorative purposes, the scheme included the over-cladding of the block using Glass Reinforced Plastic (GRP) and the installation of PVC window frames. The cladding was added mainly for decorative purposes.

1.4.2   The events of the fire

A lit cigarette was the source of the fire, which then broke through a window on the 5th floor. The fire spread through the external cladding climbed up to the next floors reaching the 12th floor within ten minutes, destroying flats on 9 floors. The cladding material used was GRP cladding. The cladding material used on the building, GRP, was ignited at the exposed edges. The cut edge of the window pods and spandrel panels provided a path of flames and hot gases from inside of the cladding.

However, the parts which were not overclad did not experience a rapid spread of the fire. There was one fatality and four injuries.

1.4.3   Response

North Ayrshire Council ordered the precautionary removal of plastic cladding and PVC window frames from other blocks following the fire at Garnock Court. A select committee inquiry into the dangers of combustible cladding on the tower block was set up on 7th December 1999, and the Committee made ten recommendations, including under no circumstances should the cladding be used on high-rise buildings. It identified the dangers of the cladding system were, fire may exit the building at one floor, spread up the building and re-enter the building at another floor. The evidence reviewed established that the focus of guidance was limited to test methods of material resistance to fire spread, and the referenced classifications in ADB – "limited combustibility" and "Class 0" – were only based on laboratory tests conducted on small samples.

The government responded to the recommendation by stating the ADB was sufficient in keeping tower blocks safe.

1.4.4   Implication

The findings of BRE from testing samples of GRP from the block confirmed it would not have achieved Class 0. In their report to the North Ayrshire Council, they recommended that the performance of any related material should be carefully assessed before it is used on high-rise residential blocks. And at the time, the new European tests should be relied upon for additional information to be gained from this test over the existing British Standard (BS 476).

The technical and procedural regulations in Scotland differ from those in England and Wales. Controls on the materials used in or on external walls existed in the Scottish Technical Standards. However, these controls were applicable at the height of 15 metres instead of the 20 metres as specified in ADB.

1.4.5   Outcome

Following a Scottish select committee review that was reported in January 2000, the Building (Scotland) Act 2003 was passed, and the introduction of The Building (Scotland) Regulations 2004 came into force on 1 May 2005. Building regulations in Scotland were significantly revised in 2005 to include "resistance to fire spread" as a functional standard for buildings. A mandatory requirement for every building to be designed and constructed in such a way as to ensure the spread of fire on external walls was inhibited in the event of an outbreak was included.

The BRE produced a method of testing for assessing the fire performance of external cladding systems, which were then proposed for the revision to ADB and to become a British Standard.

1.5   Harrow Court 2006

1.5.1   Background

In Stevenage, Hertfordshire, England, on 2 February 2005, a fire broke out in a tower block. Harrow Court was a 17-storey concrete tower block built in the mid-1960s. It had 103 flats, each floor included six apartments – four with two bedrooms and two with one bedroom. There was a permanent ventilation system for protecting the stairs, and it relied on air being drawn into the stair enclosure through the ground floor entrance doors and the openable windows because lobbies and

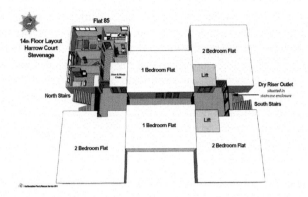

Figure 1.6 14th Floor Layout Harrow Court.

corridors did not extend to the external walls. Dry risers ran through the building with a single outlet on each floor located on the staircase landing.

In 2002, a new Fire Detection and Alarm System was added to the common areas of Harrow Court in compliance with The Building Regulations 2000, Fire Safety Approved Document B and British Standard 5588. In 2004, The Hertfordshire Fire and Rescue Service (HFRS) notified the tower block management of a number of issues affecting the means of escape and fire safety of the building and the need for remedial repairs to be carried out to eliminate potential compromise to potential fire rescue.

1.5.2   The events of the fire

The fire started on the 14th floor from a lit tealight candle which had melted through the television it was placed on. Due to the spread of fire and smoke, the escape routes rapidly deteriorated.

It was not a statutory requirement for a fire alarm and automatic fire detection (AFD) system to be provided in the common areas of buildings that contain purpose-built flats since each floor is designed as a separate fire compartment. All apartments are self-contained fire-resistant structures with fire-resistant walls separating them from other accommodations. These apartments are equipped with a fire-resistant entrance door with a self-closing mechanism. In the event of a fire, therefore, residents of the unaffected flats should be able to safely remain in their own flats without having to evacuate the entire building.

An investigation into the fire found that there was no dry riser outlet on the 14th floor of the building as they were only located on alternate floors. The firefighters connected to the dry riser on the 13th floor, but then to fight the location of the fire, the hose had to pass through fire doors, which were then kept open. This led to the fire having more oxygen due to the fact that compartmentation was compromised.

The incident resulted in the death of three people, two of whom were firefighters. The firefighters were unfamiliar with the building and its fire protection features. The two firefighters died when they got tangled in cable trays which were attached to the ceiling with plastic hooks that had melted in the fire.

Figure 1.7 Damaged Elevation of Harrow Court.

1.5.3 Stay-put policy

According to a resident, they were instructed to "stay put", but they escaped instead. However, many residents ignored the fire alarm signal, leaving others confused as to whether to evacuate or remain in the building.

There seemed to have been a perceived contradiction between notices in the common area which cautioned residents to "Leave the building by the safest available exit" while simultaneously advising, "Remain in your flat if unaffected by fire and await the arrival of the fire brigade". On the night of the incident, this caused some confusion among the residents.

It is important to note the conflict between the provision of a fire alarm in the common areas of the building with the "stay-put" fire strategy for this building, which led to residents ignoring the common fire alarm signal and remaining in their apartments at all times.

1.5.4 Outcome

The HFRS Fire Safety Department re-evaluated its entire evacuation strategy for high-rise apartments and, in particular, the apparent contradiction between the "stay put" and "evacuation" strategies. In a report, sprinklers were recommended for all tower blocks. The coroner deemed the findings of the report to be of national significance and forwarded them to the Department of Communities and Local Government (DCLG) for review. Regardless, requests to install sprinklers were rejected, and the stay-put policy remained in place.

1.6   Lakanal House 2009

1.6.1 Background

South London witnessed a fire four years after the Harrow Court fire at Lakanal House, a 14-storey tower block built in 1959 which forms part of the Sceaux Gardens Estate, Camberwell. It contained 98 flats and was 41.91 m high, fire

Figure 1.8 Damaged Elevation of Lakanal House.

alarms and sprinklers were not installed in the building's communal areas. The flats in Lakanal House are arranged in an interlocking "scissor" split-level design, a typology which was common for tower blocks during this era.

An investigation by the London Fire Brigade (LFB) found that the tower had previously been earmarked for demolition in 1999 due to a risk of a spread of fire. However, the South London Council owners of the tower block later decided against the demolition in favour of a refurbishment. Noteworthy is that as part of the 1980s refurbishment works on the building, there was a removal of vital fire-stopping material between flats and communal corridors.

Then, in 2006, a change in law made the Southwark Council responsible for ensuring fire safety in the block. This necessitated a thorough fire inspection to be carried out as a legal responsibility. Fire safety checks were to be conducted for each flat; however, as of July 2009, the Council had neither carried out checks on Lakanal House nor any other residential tower block.

There is evidence to suggest this incident was acknowledged by the industry as a further confirmation of the shortcomings of the Building Regulation and the stay-put policy.

1.6.2   The events of the fire

On 3 July 2009, a fire broke out in one of the flats of Lakanal House. The source of the fire was a faulty television in a flat on the ninth floor. The fire brigade was in attendance within six minutes of the first call. Smoke quickly filled the central stairwell, which was the only means of entering and exiting the building. The building did not have a central fire alarm or sprinkler system.

Additionally, there was a lack of compartmentation in the suspended ceilings, and the fire doors were not equipped with smoke seals. Stay put was also advised to residents despite the rapid spread of fire across floors. Theoretically, compartmentalisation was assumed to be in place and thus validating the policy. The only survivors of the fire were those who refused the stay-put guidance.

Six residents were killed in the fire, 15 residents and a firefighter were injured and another 40 residents were required to assist in the rescue effort. In addition to the deaths and injuries caused by the fire, over 90 families were forced to evacuate their homes.

1.6.3 Building regulations

Fire resistance prescribed by law should be up to 60 mins. However, the incident proved this to be about four minutes. Only two years prior to the incident, the building was refurbished with flammable material as a result of substandard and unsafe renovation work and the failure of the council to inspect the building.

Three years prior, ADB had been updated by the government. The guidance changed on cladding was small but on a significant aspect. Data testing, simulating the effects of fire, was now acceptable as opposed to full-scale testing. The principle of carrying out an assessment, in lieu of a test (also known as a desktop study), was a well-established part of the system for classifying the fire performance of construction products and systems.

1.6.4 Stay-put policy

As a result of confusion among controllers at the scene, the relevant flats were not searched in time despite the urging of relatives and neighbours of those trapped, partly because they were unfamiliar with the block's layout. Some victims were urged to remain in smoke-filled flats when they should have been evacuated.

1.6.5 Response

The ten-week hearing saw some distressing evidence leading to a series of recommendations.

1.6.6 Outcome

A series of recommendations were made by the coroner during the ten-week inquest.

High-rise blocks should be visited by fire services in order to understand their layout, and landlords should consider installing a sprinkler system. Fire safety information should also be provided to residents, and a review of the stay-put policies should be done.

The inquest found ADB to be ambiguous and unclear. It was recommended that guidance on the scope of fire risk assessments and on the building regulations should be clarified. Despite acknowledging the recommendation, the government failed to implement it.

Bibliography

App, P. (2021) Government sought to 'play down' cladding fire at pilot project it funded in 1990s, investigation reveals, [online] Available from: https://www.insidehousing.co.uk/news/news/government-sought-to-play-down-cladding-fire-at-pilot-project-it-funded-in-1990s-investigation-reveals-71116 (Accessed 29 January 2023).

Architects' Journal (2009) Lakanal House: new evidence reveals how fatal fire spread, [online] Available from: https://www.architectsjournal.co.uk/archive/lakanal-house-new-evidence-reveals-how-fatal-fire-spread (Accessed 30 January 2023).

Barling, K. (2017a) Investigation of Lakanal House Fire, [online] Available from: http://lakanalhousefire.co.uk/about/ (Accessed 30 January 2023).

Barling, K. (2017b) We've been here before, SAGE Publications: London, England, 28(3), pp. 30–35, [online] Available from: https://journals.sagepub.com/doi/abs/10.1177/0956474817730766 (Accessed 30 January 2023).

British Broadcasting Corporation (2006) Errors revealed in fire report, [online] Available from: http://news.bbc.co.uk/2/hi/uk_news/england/beds/bucks/herts/4994486.stm (Accessed 30 January 2023).British Broadcasting Corporation (2013) 'Towering inferno' fears for Gulf's high-rise blocks – BBC News, [online] Available from: https://www.bbc.com/news/world-middle-east-22346184 (Accessed 29 January 2023).

British Broadcasting Corporation (2018) The Fires that Foretold Grenfell, United Kingdom of Great Britain and Northern Ireland, [online] Available from: https://www.bbc.co.uk/programmes/b0bqjp75 (Accessed 30 January 2023).

Communities and Local Government (2009) Report to the Secretary of State by the Chief Fire and Rescue Adviser on the emerging issues arising from the fatal fire at Lakanal House, Camberwell on 3 July 2009. Communities and Local Government.

Department for Communities and Local Governments (2014) Generic Risk Assessments 3.2- Fighting Fires in High-Rise Buildings (p. 28). HMSO, Holborn, London UK.

Fire Brigades Union (2006) Executive H&S summary of 85 Harrow Court | Fire Brigades Union, [online] Available from: https://www.fbu.org.uk/publications/executive-hs-summary-85-harrow-court (Accessed 29 January 2023).

Fire Brigades Union (2019) Government deregulation responsible for Grenfell, [online] Available from: https://www.fbu.org.uk/news/2019/09/23/government-deregulation-responsible-grenfell-new-report-says (Accessed 29 January 2023).

Institute of Fire Engineers (2018) Incident Dairy 2005 – Harrow Court, [online] Available from: https://www.ife.org.uk/Firefighter-Safety-Incidents/2005-harrow-court/34309 (Accessed 29 January 2023).

Lambeth Council (2013) Lakanal House Coroner Inquest, [online] Available from: https://www.lambeth.gov.uk/about-council/transparency-open-data/lakanal-house-coroner-inquest (Accessed 30 January 2023).

Local Government Association (2011) Fire Safety in Purpose Built Blocks of Flats LGA, p. 27, UK.

London Fire and Civil Defence Authority (1999) The Irvine Fire – An Internal Briefing, [online] Available from: https://assets.grenfelltowerinquiry.org.uk/BRE00035379_DETR%27s%20file%20in%20relation%20to%20the%20fire%20at%20Garnock%20Court%20in%20Irvine%2C%20Scotland%20%28part%201%20of%202%29_0.pdf (Accessed 29 January 2023).

McKeon, C. (2021) Knowsley Heights fire was 'played down' by government, but could have been Grenfell warning, 14th June, [online] Available from: https://www.liverpoolecho.co.uk/news/liverpool-news/knowsley-heights-fire-played-down-20811871 (Accessed 29 January 2023).

Moore-Bick, M. (2019) Grenfell Tower Inquiry: Phase 1 Report Overview. Open Government Licence.

Morgan, P., Jones, D. and Clinch, S. (1991) Summary of fires investigated: April 1991 to March 1992, [online] Available from: https://assets.grenfelltowerinquiry.org.uk/BRE00035385_The%20BRE%27s%20Report%20into%20the%20fire%20at%20

Knowsley%20Heights%2C%20Liverpool%2C%20prepared%20for%20the%20 Department%20of%20the%20Environment_0.pdf (Accessed 29 January 2023).

National Archives (2004) Investigation of the fire at Knowsley Heights, Huyton, Liverpool, [online] Available from: https://discovery.nationalarchives.gov.uk/details/r/C11197377 (Accessed 29 January 2023).

National Fire Chiefs Council (2020) Simultaneous Evacuation Guidance. https://www. nationalfirechiefs.org.uk/Simultaneous-evacuation-guidance (Accessed 29 January 2023).

Phillips, I. (2009) From 21st century leisure to 20th century holiday catastrophe: the Isle of Man Summerland holiday centre fire disaster, [online] Available from: https://research. birmingham.ac.uk/en/publications/from-21st-century-leisure-to-20th-century-holiday-catastrophe-the (Accessed 29 January 2023).

Phillips, I. (2020) Summerland Fire Disaster, [online] Available from: https://www.summer-landfiredisaster.co.uk/resources/ (Accessed 29 January 2023).

UK Fire Statistics (2017) Fire Statistics, Preceding Editions, Home Office, London, https:// www.gov.uk/government/collections/fire-statistics (Accessed 29 January 2023).

2 Grenfell Tower fire

Nenpin Dimka

2.1 Introduction

This chapter explores the fall-out and failures revealed during the Hackitt Review and Grenfell Inquiry. The Grenfell Tower refurbishment commissioned by the Royal Borough of Kensington and Chelsea (RBKC) appeared to be associated with deficiencies in terms of the professional conduct of several parties involved with the project.

An explanation of the refurbishment changes made to the external cladding system to improve the building and the events of the incident are provided. Also, the Dame Judith Hackitt independent review focuses on the application of building regulations to the refurbishment project and the implications to fire safety in high-rise residential buildings (HRRBs) such as the Grenfell Tower and the need for improvements to ensure these buildings are safe to live in.

This chapter then provides insight from the Grenfell Inquiry, which revealed evidence of the characteristics of the UK construction industry as direct and indirect causes of the tragedy with disastrous consequences. Finally, evidence uncovered from the Phase 1 Inquiry is detailed, and an overview of Phase 2 is outlined.

2.2 The Grenfell fire

2.2.1 Background

The Grenfell Tower was a residential block completed in 1974 as part of the Lancaster West Estate, owned by the RBKC, and part of its provisions of social housing. It was about 68 m in height and had 25 stories – including the basement floor level and plant floor at the roof level.

The Tower was built primarily of reinforced concrete. Its structure had a single central core, reinforced concrete floors, and perimeter reinforced concrete columns, which were connected by spandrels (a horizontal section running above and below the window). The external wall was also made of solid construction with sliding windows made of aluminium and non-structural infill panels.

DOI: 10.1201/9781003357452-2

Figure 2.1 The Grenfell Tower before refurbishment works.

The storey floor space on each residential floor level 4–23 was approximately 22 m × 22 m with an approximate height floor to floor of 2.6 m on most floors. Reinforce concrete cross walls were used to partition each providing a total of 6 flats on each floor. Levels 0–3 included nursery offices and a community health centre.

2.2.2 Refurbishment

The Kensington and Chelsea Tenant Management Organisation (KCTMO), an independent company, has been responsible for the management of the tower since 2009, the owner remained the RBKC. A major refurbishment project was commissioned in 2012 to improve heating energy efficiency and external appearance. Construction commenced in 2015 and was completed in 2016.

The scope of work included extensive internal and external alteration.

Internally, seven new flats were to be created by reconfiguration of the lower floors and building services works, including the installation of a new water-based heating system, a modification of the original smoke control system into a combined environmental and smoke control system, and an extension of dry-rising fire mains. Externally, works to the tower was an over-cladding of the existing building with new insulation, new windows and new aluminium composite rain screen cladding system.

The new heating system was to supply each flat, consequently, works were undertaken on every residential lobby, which is connected to the single stair on each floor and within each flat.

The over-cladding of Grenfell Tower was a significant aspect of the scope of work. The approach of over-cladding is a well-established method used by local authorities to fulfil obligations to ensure all housing stock are energy efficient and in a state of good repair as stipulated under the Decent Homes Standard. This meant extensive improvement to the building envelope through the insulation of new air seals, new window units and overall enhancement of the appearance of the building.

Figure 2.2 The cladding on Grenfell after the refurbishment.

It is worth noting the building had prior refurbishments, including gas supply works between October 2016 and June 2017, the replacement of fire doors and entrance doors (flats) on the residential floor levels in 2011 and a replacement of the lift in 2005. The works on the gas supply were still ongoing at the time of the fire.

2.2.3   Safety concerns

The Grenfell Action Group (GAG), formed by residents of Lancaster West Estate in 2010, with the purpose of "defending the rights of the residents of Lancaster West Estate" ran a blog which challenged the council (RBKC) and management company (KCTMO) by drawing attention to significant safety issues including negligence of building maintenance and fire safety. Before the fire, an independent report carried out in 2005 highlighted issues with the emergency lighting system; similarly, in 2012, a risk assessment revealed non-compliant onsite firefighting equipment, including fire extinguishers which had expired by four years. GAG published the 2012 report and campaigned in demand of improvements to the fire safety of residential tower blocks, which was met with a threat of legal action by KCTMO.

In January 2016, GAG expressed concern that people might be trapped in the building in the event of a fire, emphasising the building's single entrance and exit, along with the corridors that had accumulated rubbish. In its warning concerning the hazards at Grenfell, the GAG frequently referred to other fires that had occurred in tower blocks.

Forty significant issues with fire safety were identified by an independent assessor in June 2016, with recommendations for actions to be carried out within weeks. In November 2016, a fire deficiency notice was issued by the London Fire and Emergency Planning Authority to KCTMO containing a list of actions, including concerns with fire doors and firefighters' lift controls. KCTMO was obligated to comply by May 2017. The Grenfell Tower fire disaster started on 14 June 2017 at 00:54 BST, causing 72 fatalities and 74 non-fatal injuries (of which 20 were critical).

2.2.4 Exterior cladding

Changes to the exterior cladding of the Grenfell Tower involved the installation of a ventilated rain screen system. The composition of the cladding system was designed to function as protection for the building from direct rainfall. The cladding system had a 50 mm air cavity behind the outer skin, which was incorporated to collect and drain rainwater.

2.2.4.1 Aluminium-polyethylene cladding

Aluminium composite panels (ACP), commonly known as Reynobond 55, comprised of a 3 mm central plastic polyethene core bonded to two 0.5 mm thick aluminium sheets, and the insulation layer was 80 mm Celotex RS500 PIR polymer form with an added 100 m layer fixed to the columns at the spandrel. Ventilation and drainage of any rainwater which might have penetrated gaps between the internal and external cladding panels were accommodated by providing a 50 mm cavity between the inside face of the rain screen panel and the outer face of the insulation. However, on the face of the insulation board and the columns, smaller cavities were also formed without any design function.

2.2.4.2 Polyisocyanurate insulation

The insulation installed was *polyisocyanurate insulation* (PIR) foams, which are able to spread flames rapidly because of their low ignition time. Furthermore, the PIR foam in the cavities accelerated the spread of fire to adjacent materials. As a result of the cavities producing chimney effects, the vertical flame spread by the upward movement of hot air in enclosed vertical spaces. The composition of the materials used played a significant role in the rate and extent of flame spread.

2.2.4.3 Cavity barriers

The cavity barriers were only installed during the over-cladding process. As a fire-preventative measure, when a fire occurs, the intumescent strip expands to seal the gap between the barrier and the rear of the cladding panels. But no cavity barriers were installed in all columns, nor at the tops of the columns nor at the heads of the rain screen cladding. The discontinuity in cavity barriers due to the presence of the cladding rails supporting the ACM panels and poor installation were found to be significant factors.

Based on the findings of the inquiry, polyethylene was the primary cause of the rapid spread of the fire.

2.2.4.4 Windows

On each floor of the tower, new window units were installed as part of the works. However, the original timber window units were in situ. The new units were smaller in size than the original windows and were finished to flush with the new

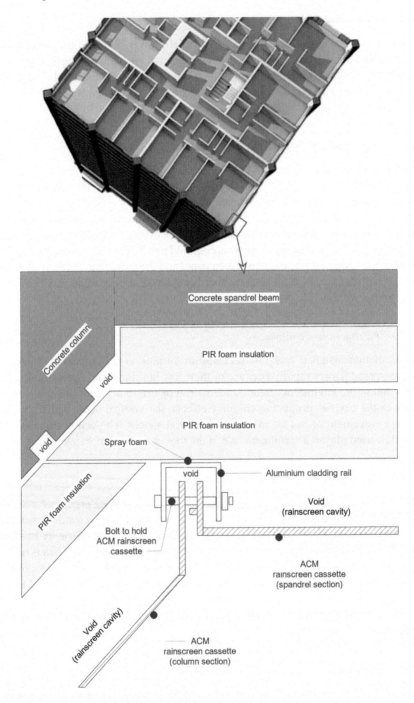

Figure 2.3 Horizontal section through the external wall system.

Figure 2.4 Potential route of fire spread into cladding cavity.

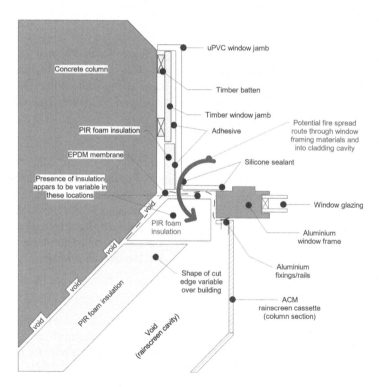

Figure 2.5 Location of new window.

over-cladding system as opposed to the original concrete, thus creating gaps behind the new window units.

The new window sills, jambs and head were made of unplasticised polyvinyl chloride (uPVC) and were glued into position as opposed to using mechanical fixings.

Gaps around the extractor fans and within the infill panels around the windows were filled with extruded polystyrene covered with aluminium foil. Extruded polystyrene is known to melt rapidly at high temperatures forming burning droplets.

2.2.4.5   *The crown*

Changes to the building's precast concrete architectural crown were also part of the refurbishment. Originally, the top of the columns and a ring of perforated free-standing concrete beams were tapered. To refurbish the tower, Reynobond 55 PE ACM cassettes were wrapped around concrete columns and beams, creating the appearance of C-shaped fins; this was purely aesthetic but created exposed edges of PE that were found everywhere in the crown around the building above level 23.

2.2.5   **The events of the fire**

2.2.5.1   *Initial fire*

A fire was reported to have started in a fridge-freezer located in Flat 16 on the fourth floor of Grenfell Tower in the early hours of the morning of 14 June 2017. The fire began to move beyond the kitchen as flame, along with resulting hot gases The uPVC jamb of the kitchen window deformed and collapsed. This created a path for the fire into the cladding system.

2.2.5.2   *Spread of fire*

There was a rapid spread of the fire across the outside of the building, both vertically up the tower columns and laterally along the cladding above and below the windows. Vertical spread was aided by PIR and phenolic foam insulation boards behind the ACM panels, while the horizontal and downward spread was aided by the dripping polyethylene emanating from the spandrel and column panels and the architectural crown of the building. The fire had engulfed the entire building in less than three hours.

2.2.5.3   *Stay put policy*

Whenever a "stay put policy" was in place for an affected building, it is recommended that the occupants only evacuate when the fire, heat or smoke adversely affects them. The concept of "stay put" has been the cornerstone of fire safety advice for high-rise multi-occupancy residential buildings since it was first introduced in 1962.

In the absence of flames, heat or smoke, it is considered safer for them to "stay put" in their own flat rather than leave the building. This principle relies on compartmentalisation to be effective, that is to say, the building must be designed and constructed to withstand the spread of fire and to provide egress and access to the building. Grenfell Tower had a "stay put" fire policy in place; however, there was minimal evidence of adequate resistance to the spread of fire.

Residents were advised in areas unaffected by the blaze to remain there, as opposed to an evacuation, even at the point when the level of smoke in the stairwell constituted a threat to life.

The fire caused 72 deaths, and the amount of smoke greatly contributed to the number of fatalities.

2.3 Hackitt Review

Following the Grenfell Tower fire, Ministers commissioned former Health and Safety Executive (HSE) chair Dame Judith Hackitt to review the current building safety regime. The independent review identified that change was needed in the current building regulations and fire safety system to make buildings safer moving forward. There was an interim report published in December 2017 and a final report published on 17 May 2018.

2.3.1 Interim report

A concern was raised in the interim report regarding the complexity of relevant regulations, the roles and responsibilities of stakeholders and the enforcement of these regulations. It highlighted the following key points:

- Current regulation and guidance were unclear.
- The clarity of roles and responsibilities in the system is unclear.
- The means of assessing and ensuring appropriate levels of competence throughout the system are unclear and inadequate.
- Enforcement and sanction measures are poor and do not provide adequate means of compliance assurance, deterrence or redress for non-compliance.
- There is a lack of a clear way for resident concerns to be raised and addressed with respect to fire safety.
- Current methods for testing, certification and marketing of construction products and systems are not clear.
- There are lessons to be learned from other international regulatory regimes.
- Leading to the conclusion that the current regulatory system was not fit for purpose in relation to high-rise and complex buildings.

The interim recommendations made were the following:

- The government should consider how the suite of Approved Documents could be structured and ordered "to provide a more streamlined, holistic view while retaining the right level of relevant technical detail", with the government asked to consider presentational changes as an interim measure.
- The related professional and accreditation bodies should work together to come up with a system to ensure those working on the design, construction, inspection and maintenance of complex and high-risk buildings are suitably qualified.
- Consultation with the fire and rescue services is required on plans for buildings that are covered by the Regulatory Reform (Fire Safety) Order 2005, but do not work as intended. Consultation by building control bodies and by those commissioning or designing buildings should take place early in the process, and fire and rescue service advice should be fully taken into account.

- It was currently the case under the 2005 Fire Safety Order that fire risk assessments for HRRBs must be carried out "regularly". It is recommended that the responsible person ensures these are undertaken at least annually and when any significant alterations are made to the building. These risk assessments should be shared in an accessible way with the residents who live within that building and notified to the fire and rescue service.
- The government should significantly restrict the use of desktop studies to approve changes to cladding and other systems to ensure that they are only used where appropriate and with sufficient, relevant test evidence. Those undertaking desktop studies must be able to demonstrate suitable competence.

2.3.2 Final report

The final report of the review sought to move forward from the interim report with the objective of addressing the systemic failure and a culture of indifference fostered in the construction industry. It sets out a new regulatory framework focused on multi-occupancy HRRBs that are ten storeys or more in height which address the issues identified in the interim report. Emphasis was made on the framework being delivered as a package and based around a series of interdependent, mutually reinforcing changes where one measure drives another.

A new regulatory framework will be developed to focus on multi-occupancy HRRBs with ten stories or more and a mandatory incident reporting mechanism for dutyholders. This will be accompanied by the formation of Joint Competent Authorities (JCAs) to ensure that all safety risks affecting these buildings are assessed, managed and monitored by local authorities, fire departments and the HSE.

As part of the recommendations, building safety will also be improved during the construction, refurbishment and design, as well as the occupation phases.

During the construction, refurbishment and design phase:

- A set of dutyholder roles and responsibilities;
- Gateway points to strengthen oversight of building construction;
- A stronger change control process to improve record keeping;
- Oversight of building standards from a single source (the JCA), with the JCA using only Local Authority Building Standards (currently Building Control);
- A greater range of enforcement powers;

During the occupation phase:

- A "clear and identifiable" dutyholder responsible for building safety of the whole building, with requirements to present information on risk management to the JCA regularly;

Inclusion of residents' voice in the system:

- Clearer rights and obligations for residents, and providing opportunities for residents to have more information, be involved in and escalate issues;

On improving levels of competencies:

- An overarching body with oversight of related competence requirements;
- There should be a long-term aim that guidance on how to meet building regulations is owned by industry while oversight and the requirements are set out by the government (with the government having the right to create guidance if industry is not able to produce suitable guidance);
- Taking forward recommendations from the Expert Group on the presentation of Approved Documents;

Creating robust and transparent construction products requires:

- A "more robust and transparent" regime for construction products through clearer and more transparent specification and testing; clear statements on what systems products can and can't be used for. Alongside this, changes to the testing regime and there should be a more effective enforcement, complaint investigation and market surveillance regime at a national level for construction products;

Golden thread:

- Creating an electronic "golden thread" record of information about the design, construction and occupation of new HRRBs;

Additionally, changes to procurement practices for HRRBs around safety requirements and consider extending this to other buildings. Finally, a recommendation that the government should rejoin the Inter-Jurisdictional Regulatory Collaboration Committee (IRCC).

2.3.3   *Outcome-based regulations*

The new regulatory framework must be outcome-based rather than based on prescriptive rules and complex guidance, and it must have real teeth so that it can drive the right behaviours – the report stated. This will create an environment where there are incentives to do the right thing and serious penalties for those who choose to game the system and, as a result, put the users of the "product" at risk.

2.4   Grenfell Tower Inquiry

2.4.1   *Introduction*

The Grenfell Tower Inquiry (Inquiry) was created to examine the circumstances leading up to and surrounding the fire at Grenfell Tower on the night of 14 June 2017.

Sir Martin Moore-Bick was appointed as the Chairman of the Public Inquiry, which was set up in August 2017. The Inquiry was separated into two phases:

1 Phase 1 focused on the factual narrative of the events on the night of 14 June 2017.
2 Phase 2 of the Inquiry examined the causes of these events, including how Grenfell Tower came to be in a condition which allowed the fire to spread in the way identified by Phase 1.

The Inquiry, under the Inquiries Act 2005, has:

- disclosed over 320,000 documents to the Core Participants;
- received over 1,600 witness statements; and
- held more than 300 public hearings.

2.4.2   Phase 1

Hearings for Phase 1 began in May 2018 and concluded in December 2018. The Chairman published his Phase 1 report on 30 October 2019.

2.4.2.1   Fire at Grenfell Tower

The first phase of hearings began with commemorations of those who lost their lives. During this phase, the Inquiry took place in parallel with an investigation that was being undertaken by the Metropolitan Police Service (MPS) and the Coroner for Inner London (West), Professor Fiona Wilcox.

As a consequence of the incident, the principles governing fire safety in HRRBs, such as the Grenfell Tower, have prompted the "stay put" strategy to be adapted in response to fires in individual flats. Furthermore, applicable guidance on compliance with the legislative requirements was discussed in relation to the original construction and subsequent refurbishment of Grenfell Tower.

With regard to the renovation work, the addition of an architectural crown, the new cladding system and changes to the windows and their surrounds were intended to promote safety in the event of a fire.

Evidently, the Lakanal House Fire contributed significantly to the background of the Grenfell Tower fire. Several recommendations for change were made following the fire, some directed at the LFB. As a result of this Fire incident, to improve 999 call handling in general and to ensure that calls requiring potentially life-saving Fire Survival Guidance (FSG) are handled correctly, the LFB conducted an intensive internal review of its practices and policies. The review questioned whether the control room balanced staying put against escaping risks and assumed firefighters could reach FSG callers quickly. Although the policy was changed, on 14th June 2017, the control room responded to the Grenfell Tower callers with similar deficiencies.

There were numerous events between 00.54 hours, when the control room first received the fire call from the Grenfell Tower, and 08.10 hours, when the last survivor left the Tower. Survivors and firefighters provide testimony, 999 call records and expert witnesses called by the Inquiry to aid in the investigation. During each period, the MPS, the London Ambulance Service, RBKC and the TMO assessed the fire's behaviour and the events on the scene and in the control room, along with the conditions inside the Tower and the actions of the occupants.

2.4.2.2 *Flat 16 fire: causes, origins and escape*

The fire started in Flat 16 due to an electrical fault in a large fridge freezer, though it was never clear what caused the fault. Regarding the spread of the fire, the cladding was likely to have been affected by hot smoke that impinged on the window jamb of the uPVC frame, causing it to collapse and deform, creating an opening through which flames and hot gases could pass into the cavity between the insulation and the ACM cladding panels. There is a possibility that flames from the fire in the fridge-freezer may have passed through the open kitchen window and intruded on the ACM cladding panels above. Firefighters testified that the fire had entered the cladding before they opened the kitchen door.

2.4.2.3 *Fire's subsequent development*

After the fire escaped from Flat 16, it spread quickly up the east face, across the building's top and engulfed the entire building in less than 3 hours. The flame fronts converged on the west face near the southwest corner of the building.

The presence of Aluminium Composite Material (ACM) rain screen panels with polyethylene cores, which served as a fuel source, it could explain the reasons why the flames spread so rapidly up, down and around the building. Due to melted and dripping polyethylene from the crown, spandrels and column panels, the fire spread horizontally and downward, starting fires lower down the building. As a result, the flame front moved diagonally across each face of the tower as those fires travelled back up the building.

ACM panels and perhaps window surrounds contributed to the rate and extent of vertical flame spread, including PIR and phenolic foam insulation boards behind them. Horizontally, the fire spread primarily through the crown while downwardly through the columns.

2.4.2.4 *Fire spreading through the tower due to loss of compartmentation*

The evidence relating to the penetration of the building by smoke and fire has been considered in light of the rapid loss of compartmentation and the spread of fire within the tower. During the fire, the fire spread quickly from the outside of the building to many flats, while smoke spread rapidly through the interior. As a result, compartmentation failed for the following reasons:

1　As a result of the intense heat, the glass in the windows failed, allowing the fire to invade the apartments.
2　Kitchen extractor fans were prone to deforming and dislodging, providing points of entry.

3 Many critical aspects of the tower's fire protection system malfunctioned, including all fire doors did not hold back smoke. Many doors lacked self-closing devices and thus failed to close. Some of these doors were broken down by fire-fighters or wedged open with firefighting equipment.

Smoke lodging was evident in many lobby areas as early as 01.20 and continued until 2.00. A considerable amount of heat and smoke was present at all levels. By 2.20, people could still use the stairs to escape despite the increased danger. By the time there was less smoke on the stairs, 168 people had escaped.

2.4.2.5 *Complying with the building regulations*

Considering the building's height, use and location, there was compelling evidence that the external walls did not adequately resist the spread of fire as per Require-ment B4(1) of Schedule 1 to the Building Regulations 2010. It was actively pro-moted instead; this is why it was considered paramount, as part of Phase 2, to investigate how those responsible for refurbishment design determined that the tower met that essential requirement.

2.4.2.6 *The planning and preparation of the LFB*

When fires spread beyond the compartment of origin in high-rise buildings, a "stay put" strategy becomes unworkable, according to the National Guidance. The inci-dent commanders should be trained to understand when partial and full evacuations may be required for any high-rise building in their area.

According to LFB policy, PN633, officers should consider evacuation arrange-ments during familiarisation visits when fighting fires in high-rise buildings. Despite this, the LFB, seemed to be inadequately prepared for a fire like the one at Grenfell Tower.

There needed to be a greater understanding of how materials and construction methods used in this high-rise building would behave and perform in a fire. Fur-thermore, LFB incident commanders needed to be trained to recognise or organise evacuations, and the Grenfell Tower needed a contingency plan which was not in place at the time of the incident.

Despite the LFB's purported existence of an operational risk database (ORD) and a risk assessment policy (PN800) that all active firefighters can access, the entry on the ORD for Grenfell Tower did not provide an incident commander with much helpful information. Many years of outdated information in the ORD did not reflect the refurbishment, and in some cases, there was inaccurate information about the tower held by the LFB.

2.4.3 *Phase 2*

Phase 2 of the Inquiry examined the causes of these events, including how Gren-fell Tower came to be in a condition which allowed the fire to spread in the way identified by Phase 1. The Phase 2 hearings, which opened in January 2020, concluded in November 2022, and the panel is preparing their final report.

The Chairman's concluding remarks included,

> Although it's possible to identify some decisions relating to the refurbishment that had an immediate effect, the wider causes of the fire had their roots in the culture of the construction industry and the regulatory regime which applies to building work, amongst other things.

Bibliography

App, P. (2021) Government sought to 'play down' cladding fire at pilot project it funded in 1990s, investigation reveals, [online] Available from: https://www.insidehousing.co.uk/news/news/government-sought-to-play-down-cladding-fire-at-pilot-project-it-funded-in-1990s-investigation-reveals-71116 (Accessed 29 January 2023).

Apps, P. (2020) Timeline: the three years since Grenfell, 6th December, [online] Available from: https://www.insidehousing.co.uk/insight/insight/timeline-the-three-years-since-grenfell-66551 (Accessed 30 January 2023).

Architects' Journal (2009) Lakanal House: new evidence reveals how fatal fire spread, [online] Available from: https://www.architectsjournal.co.uk/archive/lakanal-house-new-evidence-reveals-how-fatal-fire-spread (Accessed 30 January 2023).

Barling, K. (2017a) Investigation of Lakanal House Fire, [online] Available from: http://lakanalhousefire.co.uk/about/ (Accessed 30 January 2023).

Barling, K. (2017b) We've been here Before, SAGE Publications: London, England, 28(3), pp. 30–35, [online] Available from: https://journals.sagepub.com/doi/abs/10.1177/0956474817730766 (Accessed 30 January 2023).

Barnes, S. (2017) Inside Housing – News – Cladding can 'fail' in strong winds, Javid reveals. https://www.insidehousing.co.uk/news/cladding-can-fail-in-strong-winds-javid-reveals-52290 (Accessed 29 January 2023).

British Broadcasting Corporation (2018) The Fires that Foretold Grenfell, United Kingdom of Great Britain and Northern Ireland, [online] Available from: https://www.bbc.co.uk/programmes/b0bqjp75 (Accessed 30 January 2023).

Construction Leadership Council (2019) Raising the bar-improving competence building a safer future. Construction Leadership Council.

Fire Brigades Union (2019) Government deregulation responsible for Grenfell, [online] Available from: https://www.fbu.org.uk/news/2019/09/23/government-deregulation-responsible-grenfell-new-report-says (Accessed 29 January 2023).

Gerrard, N. (2018) Hackitt: Eight Key Recommendations – Construction Manager, [online] Available from: constructionmanagermagazine.com (Accessed 29 January 2023).

Grenfell Tower Inquiry (2023) Phase 1 report | Grenfell Tower Inquiry, [online] Available from: https://www.grenfelltowerinquiry.org.uk/phase-1-report (Accessed 30 January 2023).

Hackitt, J. (2017) Building a safer future independent review of building regulations and fire safety: interim report.

Hackitt, J. and Freng, D. (2018) Building a safer future independent review of building regulations and fire safety: final report, [online] Available from: https://assets.publishing.service.gov.uk/government/uploads/system/uploads/attachment_data/file/707785/Building_a_Safer_Future_-_web.pdf (Accessed 30 January 2023).

IH Reporters (2019) Insight – Grenfell Tower Inquiry report: full coverage, [online] Available from: https://www.insidehousing.co.uk/insight/insight/grenfell-tower-inquiry-report-full-coverage-63942 (Accessed 30 January 2023).

McKeon, C. (2021) Knowsley Heights fire was 'played down' by government, but could have been Grenfell warning, 14th June, [online] Available from: https://www.liverpoolecho.co.uk/news/liverpool-news/knowsley-heights-fire-played-down-20811871 (Accessed 29 January 2023).

Ministry of Housing, Communities and Local Government (2018) Radical reform of building regulatory system needed. 'radical reform' of building regulatory system needed, finds Dame Judith Hackitt – GOV.UK, [online] Available from: www.gov.uk (Accessed 29 January 2023).

Phillips, S. and Martin, J. (2022) Grenfell and construction industry reform: a guide for the construction professional, [online] Available from: https://www.routledge.com/Grenfell-and-Construction-Industry-Reform-A-Guide-for-the-Construction/Phillips-Martin/p/book/9780367552855 (Accessed 30 January 2023).

World Socialist Web Site (2017) UK government deregulation led to Grenfell Tower inferno, [online] Available from: https://www.wsws.org/en/articles/2017/06/21/bonf-j21.html (Accessed 29 January 2023).

3 Remediation of existing buildings

Jennifer Charlson

3.1 Introduction

In response to the pressure to remediate existing buildings, the government has responded with a number of initiatives led by the Ministry of Housing, Communities & Local Government (MHCLG), which, in September 2021, changed its name to the Department for Levelling Up, Housing and Communities (DLUHC).

The government established remediation, building safety, waking watch relief and waking watch replacement funds. A five-point plan to end unsafe cladding was followed by a move to proportionality in building safety.

There was then a shift in focus to a new plan to protect leaseholders and make industry pay for the cladding crisis including a letter from the Secretary of State to the residential property developer industry. The Residential Property Developer Tax (RPDT) then came into force, and a Building Safety Levy (BSL) was announced.

The Secretary of State subsequently wrote to freeholders, building landlords and managing agents, and the Building Safety Act 2022 (BSA) provisions relating to the remediation of existing fire safety defects came into force on 28 June 2022. Many of the UK's major housebuilders signed up to the government's Building Safety Pledge. The building safety programme has, on a monthly basis, released its data.

The first substantive decision on fire safety since Grenfell, *Martlet v Mulalley* has been reported. Just over five years after the Grenfell Tower fire, a housing association won a landmark cladding claim against a building contractor on external wall systems. In the subsequent *St James's Oncology SPC v Lendlease Construction* case, the judge found against the contractor because the constructed installation, within the Plantroom and the electrical substation, was not built to the designed fire strategy.

In addition, the newly created Recovery Strategy Unit has taken the first step in legal action against a freeholder who had not committed to remediating fire safety defects in a tower for which it was responsible.

3.2 Remediation, building safety and waking watch relief funds

The government announced a £400 million Social Sector ACM (Aluminum Composite Material) Cladding Remediation Fund in May 2018, followed by a

DOI: 10.1201/9781003357452-3

£200 million private sector fund in May 2019. A £1 billion BSF was announced in March 2020, followed by an additional investment of £3.5 billion in February 2021. A £30 million Waking Watch Relief Fund was announced in December 2020, followed by an additional £5 million in September 2021.

3.2.1   Social Sector ACM Cladding Remediation Fund

The Prime Minister announced on 16 May 2018 that the government would fully fund the removal and replacement of unsafe ACM cladding on social residential buildings of 18 m or over, owned by councils and housing associations, with costs estimated at £400 million (MHCLG, 2018).

3.2.2   Private Sector ACM Cladding Remediation Fund

On 9 May 2019, the Secretary of State announced that the government would fully fund the removal and replacement of unsafe ACM cladding on private sector residential buildings of 18 m or over, with costs estimated at £200 million (MHCLG, 2019).

3.2.3   Building safety fund

In the March 2020 budget, the government announced that it would provide £1 billion from 2020 to 2021 to support the remediation of unsafe non-ACM cladding systems on residential buildings of 18 m and over in both the private and social housing sectors (MHCLG, 2020a).

In February 2021, an additional £3.5 billion building safety investment was announced.

The government's £4.5 billion BSF re-opened, on 28 July 2022, for new applications for buildings over 18 m with cladding issues. Up to July 2022, over £1.3 billion had been allocated since the BSF's launch in 2020 (DLUHC, 2022a).

3.2.4   Waking Watch Relief Fund

On 22 December 2020, the government announced a £30 million fund to pay for the costs of installing an alarm system in buildings with unsafe cladding. On 16 September 2021, the Waking Watch Relief Fund re-opened to applications using additional £5 million funding (MHCLG, 2020b).

Common Alarms systems would enable costly waking watch measures to be replaced in buildings waiting to have unsafe cladding removed. Whilst waking watch is an acceptable risk mitigation strategy, the guidance is clear that alarms are preferable on the grounds of both safety and cost-efficiency.

3.3   Five-point plan to end to unsafe cladding

In February 2021, the government announced a five-point plan to bring an end to unsafe cladding (DLUHC, 2021):

1 Government will pay for the removal of unsafe cladding for leaseholders in all residential buildings 18 m and over (6 storeys) in England.

2 Generous finance scheme to provide reassurance for leaseholders in buildings between 11 and 18 m (4 to 6 storeys), ensuring they never pay more than £50 a month for cladding removal.
3 An industry levy and tax to ensure developers play their part.
4 A world-class new safety regime to ensure a tragedy like Grenfell never happens again.
5 Providing confidence to this part of the housing market including lenders and surveyors.

An additional £3.5 billion building safety investment was announced.

Lower-rise buildings were to gain new protection from the costs of cladding removal with a new scheme offered to buildings between 11 and 18 m. The scheme was to pay for cladding removal – where it is needed – through a long-term, low-interest, government-backed financing arrangement. Under the scheme, no lease-holder was to pay more than £50 a month towards the removal of unsafe cladding.

The Housing Secretary announced plans to introduce a "Gateway 2" developer levy. The proposed levy was to be targeted and apply when developers seek per-mission to develop certain high-rise buildings in England.

In addition, a new tax was to be introduced for the UK residential property development sector. This was to raise at least £2 billion over a decade to help pay for cladding remediation costs.

The government acknowledged that securing appropriate professional indem-nity insurance to cover the completion of EWS1 forms was a major barrier. An EWS1 certificate is an External Wall System Fire Review certificate (RICS, 2022). The government therefore committed to work towards a targeted, state-backed indemnity scheme for qualified professionals unable to obtain professional indem-nity insurance for the completion of EWS1 forms.

3.4 Proportionality in building safety

On 21 July 2021, the Independent Expert Statement on Building Safety in medium and lower rise blocks of flats was published (MHCLG, 2021a). The experts con-cluded that the government should act to remove uncertainty for residents, to reas-sure them about their safety and to correct the disproportionate reaction they had seen in some parts of the market:

1 EWS1 forms should not be a requirement on buildings below 18 m.
2 In the small number of cases where there are known to be concerns, these should be addressed primarily through risk management and mitigation.
3 There should be a clear route for residents/leaseholders to challenge costly remediation work and seek assurance that proposals are proportionate and cost-effective.
4 Government should work with the shadow Building Safety Regulator to con-sider how to implement an audit process to check that fire risk assessments are following guidelines, not perpetuating the risk aversion they were witnessing, in some instances, at the time.

5   Fire risk assessors and lenders should not presume that there is a significant risk to life unless there is evidence to support this. This would ensure that they respond only to the evidence and adopt a far more proportionate and balanced approach.

On the same day, the government responded that it would support and act on these five recommendations (MHCLG, 2021b).

3.5   New plan to protect leaseholders and make industry pay for the cladding crisis

On 10 January 2022, the government announced that it had reset its approach to building safety with a new plan to protect leaseholders and make developers and companies pay to fix the cladding crisis (DLUHC, 2022e). The four-point plan was the following:

1   Opening up the next phase of the BSF to drive forward taking dangerous cladding off high-rise buildings, prioritising the government's £5.1 billion funding on the highest risk
2   Those at fault to be held properly to account: a new team being established to pursue and expose companies at fault, making them fix the buildings they built and face commercial consequences if they refuse
3   Restoring common sense to building assessments: indemnifying building assessors from being sued and withdrawing the old, misinterpreted government advice that prompted too many buildings being declared as unsafe
4   New protections for leaseholders living in their own flats: with no bills for fixing unsafe cladding and new statutory protections for leaseholders within the Building Safety Bill

3.6   Letter from the Secretary of State to the residential property developer industry

On 10 January 2022, the Secretary of State wrote (DLUHC, 2022f) to the residential property developer industry asking them to agree to:

- make financial contributions to a dedicated fund to cover the full outstanding cost to remediate unsafe cladding on 11–18 m buildings, currently estimated to be £4 billion
- fund and undertake all necessary remediation of buildings over 11 m that they have played a role in developing
- provide comprehensive information on all buildings over 11 m which have historic safety defects and which they have played a part in constructing in the last 30 years

Should industry not come to the table and agree to a solution, the government would be forced to impose one. Clauses in the Building Safety Bill would allow the government to introduce a levy on developers of high-rise buildings, building on the 4% tax on the largest most profitable developers, which was announced in the year's Budget and expected to raise at least £2 billion over the next ten years to help pay for building safety remediation (DLUHC, 2022e).

3.7   Waking Watch Replacement Fund

On 27 January 2022, the government announced a further £27 million to fund the installation of alarms and replace costly Waking Watch measures in all buildings in England where a Waking Watch was currently in place at cost to leaseholders.

The Waking Watch Replacement Fund builds on the £35 million Waking Watch Relief Fund, which was focused on high-rise residential buildings (above 17.7 m) with unsafe cladding. The new £27 million fund extends financial support to more buildings (DLUHC, 2022b).

3.8   Consolidated Advice Note

In January 2022, the government withdrew the Consolidated Advice Note (Ministry of Housing, Communities & Local Government, 2020c) – interim guidance which had been wrongly interpreted by the industry as requiring remediation of all cladding irrespective of building height (DLUHC, 2022e).

3.9   Residential Property Developer Tax

The RPDT, which came into force on 1 April 2022, was introduced as part of a package to fund the cost of remediating cladding issues. Within UK residential development activities, annual trading profits in excess of £25 million per group are subject to 4% RPDT charge.

RPDT is intended to raise at least £2bn over a ten-year period. The government has stated that the tax should be time limited and will be repealed when its aims have been achieved (HM Revenue & Customs, 2022).

3.10   Building Safety Levy

On 13 April 2022, the government announced (DLUHC, 2022j) an expansion to the BSL. The BSL, introduced under section 58 of the BSA, will be on developers of residential buildings in England. Like the RPDT, the BSL is designed to raise revenue for the replacement of defective cladding, in addition to remediating any other historical building safety defects. The BSL is expected to be finalised in 2023 with the introduction of the "Gateway 2" stage of the new building safety regime.

The BSL was initially limited in scope to "higher risk" buildings identified by the new building safety regime. The government subsequently extended the potential scope to all residential and mixed use buildings and stated that this expansion will raise an estimated additional £3 billion for cladding remediation.

The construction of buildings within scope of the BSL will only commence once the BSL has been paid.

3.11   Remediation and funding – government response to the Select Committee reports

On 16 May 2022, the government published its response to the Levelling Up, Housing and Communities Select Committee's reports, published on 26 April 2021 and 7 March 2022, following its inquiries into cladding remediation and building safety remediation and funding in England (DLUHC, 2022i).

3.12   Letter from the Secretary of State to freeholders, building landlords and managing agents

On 27 June 2022, the Secretary of State wrote (DLUHC, 2022g) to the freeholders, building landlords and managing agents making it clear that building owners must take responsibility for remediating unsafe buildings and that any parties who continue to seek to recover costs from leaseholders in relation to historic defects will be committing a criminal offence.

The letter also confirmed that the BSF would shortly be re-opening for applications. Therefore, building owners/landlords who have not yet applied for funding should be ready to do so as soon as that happens. Landlords would be expected to take reasonable steps to obtain funding and ascertain whether any third parties (e.g. developers, manufacturers, contractors) can be pursued for the defects (or risk tenants going to the Tribunal to seek an order that any remediation costs incurred are not service charge recoverable).

3.13   Leaseholder protection

The BSA provisions relating to the remediation of existing fire safety defects came into force on 28 June 2022 and relate to all buildings that are at least 11 m or 5 storeys tall. Landlords are absolutely prohibited from seeking to recover the costs of cladding remediation as a service charge, and there will now only be very limited circumstances in which landlords can seek to recover the costs of remediating non-cladding-related fire safety defects from leaseholders. Even in circumstances where landlords can seek to recover the costs, they will be capped. Schedule 8 of the BSA details "Remediation costs under qualifying leases etc.".

The accompanying secondary legislation came into force on 21 July 2022:

- The Building Safety (Leaseholder Protections) (England) Regulations 2022
- The Building Safety (Leaseholder Protections) (Information etc.) (England) Regulations 2022

The Department for Levelling Up, Homes and Communities (2022d) published their guidance for leaseholders on 21 July 2022.

3.14   Building Safety Pledge

By July 2022, 48 of the UK's major housebuilders had signed up to the government's Building Safety Pledge, agreeing to pay to fix buildings of over 11 m in height which they developed or refurbished in the last 30 years and which have life critical fire safety defects (DLUHC, 2022c).

On 13 July 2022, the Levelling Up Secretary published a draft contract to turn these pledges into legally binding commitments for industry, leaseholders, residents and other parties to review before being finalised in August.

3.15 Building Safety Programme monthly data release

The September 2022 Building Safety Programme data was the 59th monthly data release (DLUHC, 2022h). The release reported that:

- At the end of September 2022, 95% (462) of all identified high-rise residential and publicly owned buildings in England had either completed or started remediation work to remove and replace unsafe ACM cladding (98% of buildings identified at 31 December 2019, 98% of buildings identified at 31 December 2020) – no change since the end of August.
- 438 buildings (90% of all identified buildings) no longer have unsafe ACM cladding systems – no change since the end of August. 389 (80% of all buildings) have completed ACM remediation works – an increase of four since the end of August. This includes 345 (71% of all buildings) which have received building control sign off – an increase of five since the end of August.
- Of those with ACM cladding remaining, 24 have started remediation. Of the 24 (5%) buildings yet to start, 2 are vacant, so do not represent a risk to resident safety, and 14 additional buildings were identified after 31 December 2020.
- 100% (160) of social sector buildings have either completed or started remediation. Of these, 159 (99%) have had their ACM cladding removed.
- 91% (210) of private sector buildings have either completed or started remediation. Of these, 194 (84%) have had their ACM cladding removed.
- £29.8 million of funding has been approved from the Waking Watch Relief and Replacement Funds covering 369 buildings and 26,900 leasehold dwellings.

3.16 Fire safety cladding case

In 2022, *Martlet v Mulalley* was the first substantive decision on fire safety since Grenfell. A housing association won a landmark cladding claim against a building contractor in the Technology and Construction Court (TCC) on external wall systems (EWS) just over five years since the Grenfell Tower fire.

3.16.1 Background

Five high-rise towers were built in Gosport, Hampshire, in the early 1960s to provide social housing. In 2005 the defendant contractor (Mulalley) was retained via a design and build contract made under deed to refurbish the towers. The main objectives of the refurbishment were to improve resistance to cold and damp penetration.

Mulalley installed a "StoTherm Classic" EWS manufactured by German company StoTherm. This comprised combustible expanded polystyrene (EPS) insulation boards, two acrylic organic non-cementitious render coats and horizontal mineral wool fire barriers. The towers achieved practical completion at different times between December 2006 and April 2008.

Nine days after the Grenfell tragedy in June 2017, the claimant housing association (Martlet) began investigating this cladding. This revealed the combustible EPS boards and installation defects to the fire barriers and EPS boards. Martlet immediately implemented a 24-hour Waking Watch patrol to protect residents and then replaced the system with a non-combustible alternative using stone wool insulation panels (the replacement works). The Waking Watch remained until the combustible cladding had been removed.

In December 2019, after losing an adjudication, Martlet issued court proceedings against Mulalley for the £8 million costs of the replacement works and Waking Watch for four of the towers. It claimed these were caused by Mulalley's installation breaches; that is, workmanship breaches. No claim was brought in relation to one tower because the 12-year limitation period since practical completion had expired. (The limitation period for claims such as these in relation to refurbishment works, if brought under the Defective Premises Act 1972 has now been extended to 15 years by the Building Safety Act 2022.)

Mulalley admitted to some installation defects but disputed the extent and denied they were the real cause for the replacement works and the Waking Watch. It argued that the real cause was Martlet's realisation, triggered in no small part by the Grenfell disaster, of the risk posed by the combustible insulation not meeting the heightened fire safety standards, which had come into force after the works had been completed.

Mulalley also argued that a less expensive repair (rather than replacement) solution would have sufficed to remedy the installation breaches. It contended that the claimed costs were irrecoverable because Martlet chose to replace, rather than to repair, which therefore represented a failure to mitigate its loss.

Martlet, in response to this argument, obtained permission to plead in the alternative to installation breaches, a failure to specify a compliant EWS; that is, the EWS did not meet applicable fire safety standards at the date of the contract (in other words a design breach was now in the pleading). Martlet contended that the replacement works and Waking Watch costs were also caused by the specification breach.

3.16.2   Decision on breach

The court held that Martlet had proven both the installation and specification breach cases.

As regards the installation breaches, the parties' architectural experts agreed that the works did not comply with the relevant fire safety requirements and standards. The fire engineering experts reached essentially the same agreement.

The specification breach case was considered on the hypothetical basis that the installation breaches did not exist. By doing so, an assessment could be made as to whether the specification breaches would have justified replacement in any event.

BBA (British Board of Agrément) Certificate 95/3132 issued in 1995 covered the StoTherm Classic system. It confirmed that the system met the functional requirement B4(1) of the Building Regulations 2000 due to the inclusion of fire barriers. The judge said the certificate was not a "guarantee" of compliance with the building regulations. He accepted that in the "real world" professional designers would place great weight on the existence of the certificate and this was relevant when considering potential professional negligence, but it did not carry "significant weight" as regards the strict design and material obligations in the contract.

Mullaley was contractually required to ensure its system complied with BR 135 (2003), which sets out the criteria and fire spread performance characteristics that cladding must meet in a fire test. This recommended that a system comprising combustible thermoplastic EPS insulants and an organic surface render should not be specified for high-rise buildings unless it had been shown to meet the performance standard in Annex A of BR 135 (2003) via a BS 8414-1 test.

It would not have been possible "for the conscientious specifier" to be satisfied that the StoTherm Classic system could properly have been specified in this case without having met that standard. Mullaley had not provided any evidence which demonstrated that the StoTherm Classic system passed the Annex A performance criteria. There was no evidence that Mullaley ever believed it would have passed.

A question for the reasonably competent designer or specifier was whether it was sufficient that the StoTherm Classic system incorporated fire barriers which appeared to comply with the design principles within BR 135 (2003), even though it had not been demonstrated that this met the Annex A performance criteria. For a contractor such as Mulalley, constructing a high-rise residential building, that would not have been enough given there were alternatives in the market which either had passed or would pass a BS 8414-1 test. Since Mulalley has been unable to identify particular features of the StoTherm Classic system, which made it more appropriate for use for other, non-fire safety reasons which outweighed the fire safety perspective, then the use of that system contravened its absolute contractual obligations.

The judge concluded that, given all of the above issues in the specification breach case, the system failed to satisfy functional requirement B4(1). The judge also considered the test for professional negligence in *Bolam v Friern Hospital Management Committee* in the context that it was common at the time of the contract to specify the StoTherm Classic system even for high-rise residential buildings. He said the "argument that 'everyone else was doing it' does not, on a proper application of the '*Bolam*' principle, operate as a get out of jail free card". It was not enough to prove that others were just as negligent and especially where perhaps not "everyone" was doing it and others were selecting an EWS that was compliant.

3.16.3 Recoverable losses

Had Martlet succeeded only on the installation breach case, it could only have recovered the cost of repair, not replacement. However, as Martlet succeeded on the specification breach case, it was entitled to recover the entire replacement works costs.

The Waking Watch costs were also recoverable in relation to the specification breach case. These costs were held to be not too remote and in any event were a reasonable step in mitigating the far greater loss which would have flowed from an evacuation of the towers.

The court indicated that Martlet would also have been able to recover Waking Watch costs had it only succeeded on the installation breach case but they would have been assessed for a lesser time period.

3.16.4   Analysis

This ruling is of interest to all those involved in the construction industry. Although this was contract and fact specific, the key points of interest are:

1   The BBA certificates issued for the system in question could not be said to "amount to a form of 'guarantee' or 'passport' to compliance with the building regulations". The decision to playdown the relevance of the certificates where the contractor had a strict contractual obligation is in line with Dame Judith Hackitt's comments about the need for greater rigour in the construction industry in her review of the building regulations following the Grenfell fire.
2   The judge was influenced in finding for the claimant in relation to the specification breaches by the fact that there was a lack of evidence of compliance provided by the contractor; that is, no successful BS 8414 test evidence was presented. He was not satisfied on the balance of probabilities, and based on the expert evidence available, the system would have passed the testing. He concluded on this point that "in a case such as this the only way of clearly demonstrating compliance or non-compliance with the performance standard is to carry out a BS 8414-1 test". Alternatively, it is acceptable to match the make-up of a successful test rig.
3   The judge found there was a strict contractual obligation to comply with the building regulations. The relevant clause in the contract is a common amendment which states that "the Contractor hereby accepts responsibility for the design of the Works and every part thereof and for the selection and standards of all and any materials, goods and workmanship forming part thereof".
4   Having succeeded on its case for specification breaches, the claimant was held to be entitled to recover its entire loss including full replacement costs and Waking Watch costs. However, if it had only succeeded on the installation breaches, then its recoverable losses would have been limited to the repair costs, not replacement costs, and a portion of the costs of the Waking Watch.

3.17   Fire safety defects case

The 2022 case *St James's Oncology SPC v Lendlease Construction* concerned alleged fire safety and electrical engineering defects in the basement plantroom (the Plantroom) of an oncology centre (the Centre), which had been designed and built at a hospital, as part of a PFI (Private Finance Initiative) project. The Technology and Construction Court (TCC) found against Lendlease Construction because the constructed installation within the Plantroom and the electrical substation were not built to the designed fire strategy.

3.17.1 Background

The defects allegations mainly related to the compartmentation and fire safety of the plant and equipment in the Plantroom and the electrical systems which served them.

The claimant was St James' Oncology SPC Limited, the Project Company (Project Co) in the PFI scheme. The defendants comprised Lendlease Construction (Europe) Limited, the design and build contractor (the Contractor), engaged by Project Co under a design and build contract (the D&B Contract) for the design and construction of the Centre, and its parent company guarantor.

The Plantroom housed three transformer rooms, two generator rooms, five switchrooms and two mechanical risers. The original fire strategy for the Plantroom at the start of the construction of the Centre (the Revision 12 Fire Strategy) provided that each room and riser would be a separate fire compartment, with its own compartmentation. However, towards the end of the construction period, the Contractor produced a revised fire strategy (the Revision 19 Fire Strategy), which detailed the whole Plantroom as one single fire compartment. The Revision 19 Fire Strategy also showed the internal walls of the rooms comprising the Plantroom as non-compartment/internal partition walls, which had openings in them for services to pass through.

Project Co contended that the Revision 19 Fire Strategy's conversion of the Plantroom from numerous fire compartments into a single fire compartment was not fire safe and that it contravened the requirements (the Requirements) of a number of NHS Health Technical Memoranda (HTMs), Building Regulations and British Standards, which Requirements were individual obligations of the Contractor under the D&B Contract. Project Co therefore maintained the Contractor's failures to meet the Requirements placed the Contractor in breach of many of the terms of the D&B Contract and liable for damages and indemnities.

At trial, the Contractor admitted some of the alleged defects but denied the others and advanced the "Fire Strategy Defence". The Contractor argued that the NHS Trust and its Fire Officer, the Project Co, the Building Inspector, the local Fire Service and the Independent Certifier for the PFI scheme had all approved the proposals in the Revision 19 Fire Strategy (issued by the Contractor towards the end of the construction phase of the Centre) for the conversion of Plantroom into a single fire compartment and that the relevant Requirements of the D&B Contract had been derogated from or varied accordingly.

3.17.2 Decision on breach

The TCC rejected the Fire Strategy Defence, finding that the changes to the Revision 12 Fire Strategy in the Revision 19 Fire Strategy had not been approved by the Trust or Project Co or any of the other parties mentioned above. They had not been provided with clear proposals for variations to the original Requirements of the HTMs, Building Regulations or British Standards. The TCC found that the Revision 19 Fire Strategy had actually been produced by the Contractor, simply to reflect the as-built condition of the Plantroom which it had already constructed.

3.17.3   *Recoverable losses*

The TCC held that the extensive remedial scheme contended for by Project Co's experts (which involved introducing fire compartmentation and re-cabling the electrical systems) was necessary to meet the contractual Requirements of the D&B Contract.

3.18   First legal action launched to keep residents safe

The Department for Levelling Up, Housing and Communities (2022k), on 9 October 2022, took the first step in legal action against Grey GR, an organisation ultimately owned by RailPen.

Grey GR Limited Partnership, the freeholder of Vista Tower, a 15-storey tower block in Stevenage, was given 21 days to commit to remediating the tower's fire safety defects or an application would be made to the courts.

The action followed two years of delays for more than 100 residents living in the tower and reaffirmed the government's commitment to making sure building owners, landlords and developers meet their legal obligations and protect tenants in their own homes.

The freeholder is one of the first to face action by the newly created Recovery Strategy Unit, set up to identify and pursue firms who repeatedly refuse to fix buildings, working closely with other enforcement authorities.

The Department for Levelling Up, Housing and Communities (2022l) has published guidance about legal protections for leaseholders from historical building safety costs including step-by-step guidance to remediation orders.

References

Cases

Bolam v Friern Hospital Management Committee [1957] 2 All ER 118.
Martlet Homes Limited v Mulalley & Co. Limited [2022] EWHC 1813 (TCC).
St James's Oncology SPC Limited v Lendlease Construction (Europe) Limited & Another [2022] EWHC 2504 (TCC).

Websites

DLUHC (2021) Government to bring an end to unsafe cladding with multi-billion pound intervention, [online] Available from: https://www.gov.uk/government/news/government-to-bring-an-end-to-unsafe-cladding-with-multi-billion-pound-intervention (Accessed 26 October 2022).

DLUHC (2022a) Press release: Leaseholders protected from unfair bills to make homes safe, [online] Available from: https://www.gov.uk/government/news/leaseholders-protected-from-unfair-bills-to-make-homes-safe (Accessed 31 August 2022).

DLUHC (2022b) Guidance Waking Watch Replacement Fund, [online] Available from: https://www.gov.uk/guidance/waking-watch-replacement-fund (Accessed 31 August 2022).

DLUHC (2022c) Building safety: developer remediation contracts, [online] Available from: https://www.gov.uk/government/publications/building-safety-developer-remediation-contracts (Accessed 1 September 2022).

DLUHC (2022d) Guidance – Building safety leaseholder protections: guidance for leaseholders, [online] Available from: https://www.gov.uk/guidance/building-safety-leaseholder-protections-guidance-for-leaseholders (Accessed 25 August 2022).

DLUHC (2022e) Government sets out new plan to protect leaseholders and make industry pay for the cladding crisis, [online] Available from: https://www.gov.uk/government/news/government-sets-out-new-plan-to-protect-leaseholders-and-make-industry-pay-for-the-cladding-crisis (Accessed 26 October 2022).

DLUHC (2022f) Letter from the DLUHC Secretary of State to the residential property developer industry on a new approach to building safety, [online] Available from: https://www.gov.uk/government/publications/letter-from-the-dluhc-secretary-of-state-to-the-residential-property-developer-industry-on-a-new-approach-to-building-safety (Accessed 26 October 2022).

DLUHC (2022g) Letter from the Secretary of State to freeholders, building landlords and managing agents, [online] Available from: https://assets.publishing.service.gov.uk/government/uploads/system/uploads/attachment_data/file/1085881/27.06.2022_letter_to_trade_bodies_on_leaseholder_protections.pdf (Accessed 4 November 2022).

DLUHC (2022h) Building Safety Programme: monthly data release – September 2022, [online] Available from: https://www.gov.uk/government/publications/building-safety-programme-monthly-data-release-september-2022 (Accessed 9 November 2022).

DLUHC (2022i) Policy paper – Building safety: remediation and funding – government response to the Select Committee reports, [online] Available from: https://www.gov.uk/government/publications/building-safety-remediation-and-funding-government-response-to-the-select-committee-reports/building-safety-remediation-and-funding-government-response-to-the-select-committee-reports (Accessed 9 November 2022).

DLUHC (2022j) Agreement with major developers to fund building safety repairs, [online] Available from: https://www.gov.uk/government/news/agreement-with-major-developers-to-fund-building-safety-repairs (Accessed 9 November 2022).

DLUHC (2022k) First legal action launched to keep residents safe, [online] Available from: https://www.gov.uk/government/news/first-legal-action-launched-to-keep-residents-safe (Accessed 13 November 2022).

DLUHC (2022l) Guidance: Making sure remediation work is done, [online] Available from: https://www.gov.uk/guidance/making-sure-remediation-work-is-done#how-does-this-affect-me-the-leaseholder (Accessed 13 November 2022).

HM Revenue & Customs (2022) Residential property developer tax manual, [online] Available from: https://www.gov.uk/hmrc-internal-manuals/residential-property-developer-tax-manual/rpdt01100 (Accessed 9 November 2022).

MHCLG (2018) Social Sector ACM Cladding Remediation Fund: application guidance, [online] Available from: https://www.gov.uk/government/publications/social-sector-acm-cladding-remediation-fund-application-guidance (Accessed 31 August 2022).

MHCLG (2019) Private Sector ACM Cladding Remediation Fund: application guidance, [online] Available from: https://www.gov.uk/government/publications/private-sector-acm-cladding-remediation-fund-prospectus (Accessed 31 August 2022).

MHCLG (2020a) Guidance: Remediation of non-ACM buildings, [online] Available from: https://www.gov.uk/guidance/remediation-of-non-acm-buildings (Accessed 31 August 2022).

MHCLG (2020b) Guidance: Waking Watch Relief Fund, [online] Available from: https://www.gov.uk/guidance/waking-watch-relief-fund (Accessed 31 August 2022).

MHCLG (2020c) Guidance: Waking Watch Relief Fund Guidance: Building safety advice for building owners, including fire doors, [online] Available from: https://www.gov.uk/government/publications/building-safety-advice-for-building-owners-including-fire-doors (Accessed 26 October 2022).

MHCLG (2021a) Independent Expert Statement on Building Safety in medium and lower rise block of flats, [online] Available from: https://www.gov.uk/government/publications/independent-expert-statement-on-building-safety-in-medium-and-lower-rise-block-of-flats (Accessed 26 October 2022).

MHCLG (2021b) Proportionality in building safety, [online] Available from: https://www.gov.uk/government/speeches/proportionality-in-building-safety (Accessed 26 October 2022).

RICS (2022) Cladding External Wall System (EWS) FAQs, [online] Available from: https://www.rics.org/uk/news-insight/latest-news/fire-safety/cladding-qa/ (26 October 2022).

4 Legal framework

Jennifer Charlson

4.1 Introduction

The Building Safety Act (BSA) 2022, which received Royal Assent on 28 April 2022, is the most significant legislation following the Grenfell Tower fire. The BSA makes ground-breaking reforms to give residents and homeowners more rights, powers and protections. In accordance with the outline transition plan, a number of changes have been implemented with the bulk of the new provisions due to come into force 12 to 18 months after Royal Assent.

The leaseholder protections in the BSA are in force with new financial protections for leaseholders in buildings above 11 m or 5 storeys with historical safety defects. The BSA has extended existing rights under the Defective Premises Act 1972 and the Building Act 1984. Building liability, remediation and contribution orders are also in force.

Rights of action against construction product manufacturers in relation to domestic properties which are unfit for habitation and for breach of the Building Regulations will be brought in force. The BSA has removed the approved inspectors insurance provision of the Building Act 1984 and strengthened the powers that the Architects Registration Board has under the Architects Act 1997. Building and Construction Products Regulations have been amended.

The Fire Safety Act 2021 and The Fire Safety (England) Regulations 2022 have come into force. The Regulatory Reform (Fire Safety) Order 2005 has been strengthened.

4.2 Building Safety Act 2022

The Building Safety Act 2022, which received Royal Assent on 28 April 2022, implements ground-breaking reforms to give residents and homeowners more rights, powers and protections (DLUHC, 2022).

It delivers protections for qualifying leaseholders from the costs associated with remediating historical building safety defects and measures that will allow those responsible for building safety defects to be held to account.

It overhauls existing regulations and makes clear how residential buildings should be constructed, maintained and made safe. The government aims to ensure

DOI: 10.1201/9781003357452-4

building regulations are fit for purpose across the built environment and where appropriate will apply the new approaches in the BSA to all building work, not just those in scope of the new regulatory regime.

The BSA created three new bodies to provide effective oversight of the new regime: the Building Safety Regulator, the National Regulator of Construction Products and the New Homes Ombudsman.

Many of the detailed provisions in the BSA will be implemented over the next two years through a programme of secondary legislation.

4.2.1   Protecting leaseholders

Building owners will not legally be able to charge qualifying leaseholders for any costs in circumstances where a building (in the majority of cases meaning those over 5 storeys or 11 m tall) requires cladding to be removed or remediated.

Qualifying leaseholders will also have protections from the costs associated with non-cladding defects, including interim measures like waking watches.

4.2.2   Residents of higher-risk buildings and homeowners

Residents in high-rise buildings will have more say in how their building is kept safe and will be able to raise building safety concerns directly with the owners and managers of their buildings (known as accountable persons) who are responsible for repairing the common parts of a higher-risk building, as defined in section 72 of the BSA. The accountable person(s) will have a duty to consider their representations and concerns.

If residents feel their concerns are being ignored, they can raise them with the Building Safety Regulator.

All homeowners will also have more than twice the amount of time, from 6 to 15 years, to claim compensation for sub-standard construction work.

4.2.3   Building owners

Dutyholders such as the Principal Designer and Principal Contractor under the BSA will be required to manage building safety risks, with clear lines of responsibility during the design, construction and completion of all buildings.

Accountable persons will need to demonstrate that they have effective, proportionate measures in place to manage building safety risks in the higher-risk buildings for which they are responsible. Those who do not meet their obligations may face criminal charges.

The BSA is also clear that building owners and landlords will need to contribute to the costs of fixing their own buildings.

4.2.4   Built environment industry

The BSA will create a framework for the design, construction and management of safer, high-quality homes. It will strengthen the construction products regulatory regime, with new requirements to make sure all construction products on the UK market are safe for their intended use, with a National Regulator for Construction Products to monitor and enforce.

There will be a new developer tax and a levy on developers.

New rights to redress will ensure those responsible for contributing to the building safety crisis will be liable for costs to rectify their mistakes.

4.2.5 Overview

The BSA has six Parts and contains provisions intended to secure the safety of people in or about buildings and to improve the standard of buildings.

- Part 2 contains provision about the building safety regulator and its functions in relation to buildings in England.
- Part 3 amends the Building Act 1984. Amendments made by Part 3 –
  a provide that the regulator is the building control authority in relation to higher-risk buildings in England, and
  b require the regulator (for England) and the Welsh Ministers (for Wales) to establish and maintain registers of building control approvers and building inspectors.
- Part 4 is about occupied higher-risk buildings in England and imposes duties on accountable persons.
- Part 5 contains further provisions, including –
  a provisions about remediation and redress;
  b provision requiring a new homes ombudsman scheme to be established;
  c powers to make provision about construction products;
  d further provision about fire safety;
  e provision about the regulation of architects;
  f provision about housing complaints.
- Part 6 contains general provisions.

4.2.6 Outline transition plan

Following Royal Assent (28 April 2022), the intention was that a number of changes would come into force within the first 12 months (MHCLG, 2021). These included:

- Establishing the Residents' Panel within the Building Safety Regulator
- Extending the limitation period of the Defective Premises Act 1972 retrospectively – and applying this Act to refurbishments prospectively
- Additional powers for the regulation of construction products, including paving the way for a national regulator for construction products, which is being established within the Office of Product Safety and Standards (OPSS)
- Changes to the Regulatory Reform (Fire Safety) Order 2005
- Strengthening the powers of the Architects Registration Board to monitor the competence of architects
- Removal of the Democratic Filter for social housing residents

Within 12–18 months of the Bill receiving Royal Assent, the intention was that the bulk of the new provisions brought forward in the Bill would come into force including:

- Establishing the Building Advisory Committee within the Building Safety Regulator to help it perform its functions to oversee the safety and performance of all buildings. Additionally, the Building Safety Regulator will begin managing the performance of building control bodies
- Setting up the Industry Competence Committee within the Building Safety Regulator to help it perform its functions to assist and encourage the improvement of competence in the built environment industry
- New Gateways to ensure rigorous assessment of regulatory requirements to ensure building safety and regulatory compliance is considered at each stage of a building's design and construction
- A targeted developer levy, which will apply only when developers seek building control approval to develop certain high-rise residential and other in scope buildings in England
- Mandatory reporting to the new Building Safety Regulator of prescribed fire and structural safety occurrences
- The requirement to create, hold and maintain the golden thread of information
- Mandatory registration of building inspectors and building control approvers
- Mandatory registration of occupied high-rise residential buildings with the Building Safety Regulator
- New requirements on dutyholders to have clear accountability and statutory responsibilities as buildings are designed, constructed and refurbished
- New duties on the Accountable Person to manage building safety risks in occupied high-rise buildings, including duties to engage with residents
- New duties on residents to ensure each other's safety by making sure their actions do not adversely affect the safety of their building
- New measures to protect leaseholders, by placing additional duties on the Accountable Person to explore alternative cost recovery routes before passing costs to leaseholders and a Building Safety Charge to cover the ongoing costs of implementing the new regime, giving leaseholders assurance, transparency and protection in relation to ongoing costs
- New requirements for construction products included on the safety-critical list and the requirement for construction products to be safe, with strengthened oversight and enforcement powers to be used by the national regulator for construction products to operate effectively.

4.2.7 Commencement

Provisions of the BSA have been brought into force by the following commencement regulations.

The Building Safety Act 2022 (Commencement No. 1, Transitional and Saving Provisions) Regulations 2022 were made on 19 May 2022. The statutory instrument contains regulations which state that certain provisions come into force on 28 May, 28 June, 28 July and 1 October 2022.

The Building Safety Act 2022 (Commencement No. 2) Regulations 2022 were made on 31 August 2022. These regulations brought sections 126 to 129 of the BSA (building industry schemes and prohibitions on development and building control) into force on 1 September 2022.

The Building Safety Act 2022 (Commencement No. 3 and Transitional Provision) Regulations 2022 were made on 18 November 2022. The following provisions of the BSA came into force on 1 December 2022:

a   sections 4(1), (2), (3) and (4) (regulator's duty to facilitate building safety)
b   sections 9(1) and (2) (building advisory committee)
c   section 11 (residents' panel)

Further provisions of the BSA will be brought into force by subsequent commencement regulations.

4.3   Leaseholder protection

The leaseholder protections in the BSA came into force on 28 June 2022, with new financial protections for leaseholders in buildings above 11 m or 5 storeys with historical safety defects.

The Building Safety (Leaseholder Protections) (England) Regulations 2022 came into force on 20 July 2022. This statutory instrument contains 13 regulations including those relating to leaseholder owned buildings (regulation 2) and remediation contribution orders (regulation 4).

The Building Safety (Leaseholder Protections) (Information etc.) (England) Regulations 2022 came into force on 21 July 2022. This statutory instrument made regulations pursuant to various powers in the BSA including those contained in section 123 (remediation orders) and in Schedule 8, specifically paragraphs 12 (recovery of service charge amounts from landlords), 13 (presumptions: qualifying leases) and 15 (information from tenants).

4.4   Limitation

The BSA has extended existing rights under the Defective Premises Act 1972(DPA).

4.4.1   *Former limitation periods*

Former limitation periods were as follows:

• Contract - 6 or 12 years from breach (completion)
• Tort - 6 years from damage or 3 years from knowledge (15 years longstop)
• Defective Premises Act 1972 – 6 years from completion

4.4.2   *New limitation periods for Defective Premises Act 1972 claims*

The implementation of section 135 of the BSA, on 28 June 2022, brought into force changes to the limitation periods for claims brought under the DPA (and section 38 of the Building Act 1984). The DPA obligates those constructing any dwelling do so in a workmanlike manner using proper materials so that, when completed, the dwelling is fit for habitation.

The reform, one of the most controversial aspects of the BSA, will require businesses in the construction industry to review their positions under the new regime.

The BSA amends the limitation period in which a potential claimant can bring a claim under the DPA from six years from completion of a dwelling to either a 30-year limitation period for dwellings completed before 28 June 2022 or 15 years for dwellings to be completed after 28 June 2022.

The BSA also introduces a new prospective right of action against any person who "takes on work in relation to any part" of a dwelling. This means that claims may now be brought in respect of any refurbishment or remedial works completed on an existing building after 28 June 2022, subject to the new 15-year limitation period.

This represents a widening of the scope for potential liability, often long after the right to bring an action under contract or in negligence has expired. Importantly, for dwellings completed as far back as June 1992, it opens up the possibility of a claim under the DPA that prior to the introduction of the BSA would have been considered time barred.

In summary, the new limitation periods for DPA claims are:

- 15 years from completion of works (or rectification works) for both:
  - New construction projects (s1 DPA)
  - Upgrade/refurbishment/rectification projects (new s2A DPA)
- 30 years for existing projects (s1 DPA)
  - Unless breach of "Convention rights" i.e. Human Rights Act 1998 (s4B Limitation Act 1980 as amended by s135 BSA

4.4.3   *Defective Premises Act 1972 claims*

The relevant provision of the DPA is:

s1 Duty to build dwellings properly.
1 A person taking on work for or in connection with the provision of a dwelling (whether the dwelling is provided by the erection or by the conversion or enlargement of a building) owes a duty –

a if the dwelling is provided to the order of any person, to that person; and
b without prejudice to paragraph (a) above, to every person who acquires an interest (whether legal or equitable) in the dwelling;

to see that the work which he takes on is done in a workmanlike or, as the case may be, professional manner, with proper materials and so that as regards that work the dwelling will be fit for habitation when completed.

The new section 2A of the DPA adds these provisions:

- equivalent s1 duties – anyone who "takes on work"
  - owes duty to employer and anyone who acquires an interest
  - to see work done in a workmanlike manner with proper materials so that the dwelling is fit for habitation

It is important to note that this new section extends to any works to existing buildings (rectification/upgrade works) not just initial "provision".

4.4.4   Defective Premises Act 1972 case

Whilst the amendments to the DPA have been brought in the context of building safety, case law has established that scope for potential claims under the DPA is broad. Potential claims include not just safety defects, but any defect or collection of defects which, on completion, make a dwelling unfit for habitation – including, for example, defects that cause distress or inconvenience to occupants.

Rendlesham Estates v Barr Ltd [2014] subjected the Defective Premises Act 1972 to judicial interpretation. An apartment block in Concord Street, Leeds, was built "on the cheap". There were poor-quality finishes and widespread defective works leading to leaking and mould issues. An adjudication on defects found in favour of the developer City Wall Limited (CWC). However, CWC went into administration without rectifying the issues. Therefore, 120 owners brought claims directly against the contractor Barr Ltd under s1 DPA for £14 million rectification works.

The issues were whether the work was "provision" of a dwelling, had the work been carried out in a workmanlike manner with proper materials and was the dwelling fit for habitation.

"For a dwelling to be fit for habitation within the meaning of the Act, it must, on completion,

a   be capable of occupation for a reasonable time without risk to the health and safety of the occupants: where the dwelling is or is part of a newly constructed building, what is a reasonable time will be a question of fact
b   be capable of occupation for a reasonable time without undue inconvenience or discomfort to the occupants"

The judge's findings included that all defects should be considered in the round, not in isolation and condition at time of completion. Reference should be to standards at time of build and the dwelling fit for habitation by all types of persons. Serious inconvenience may make a dwelling unfit even if there are no safety issues. The judge held Barr liable to the owners for breach of s1 of the DPA.

4.4.5   Considerations for works completed before 28 June 2022

Developers and contractors should review their residential portfolios. Contractors could identify any "at risk" developments in particular, those projects where limitation periods under contract have already expired, but exposure to liability under the DPA has now re-appeared. Developers, investors and building owners may wish to reconsider any claim considered to be time barred.

The BSA provides for a one year "initial period" for claims close to limitation in 2022, allowing until June 2023 to commence proceedings. For claims relating to any such developments, many of which will have been completed between 12 and 30 years ago, a particular challenge for claimants and defendants will be proving the condition of the property at completion. Businesses might consider the extent of available evidence in preparation. Documents should be retrieved and retained where possible.

There are two very limited safeguards for defendants:

1 A claim could be dismissed if it breaches a defendant's human rights. While such a defence could arguably apply where a right to a fair trial is denied due to lack of project records, the position is yet to be tested in the courts.
2 The changes do not apply to any claim which was previously settled or subject to final determination by a court or arbitrator. Parties often include "full and final" drafting in settlement agreements to exclude future claims. However, each agreement would need to be reviewed on its own merits.

4.4.6   *Considerations for works completed after 28 June 2022*

Businesses should consider whether they have sufficient warranty and insurance protection to cover the extended limitation period for existing projects. Parties may be exposed where the limitation for liability under the DPA extends beyond existing warranties and insurance policies agreed under contract. Supply chain warranties should also be considered.

When negotiating new contracts, businesses should consider the new limitation periods, identifying and apportioning risk for defect liability under the DPA and ensure that sufficient guarantee, warranty and insurance protections are in place.

Records should be retained for the duration of the relevant liability period (noting that the liability period may reset on completion of any remedial or refurbishment works). This may involve reconsidering document retention policies.

4.5   Building liability and remediation orders

On 28 June 2022, building liability, remediation and remediation contribution orders were brought into force.

4.5.1   *Building liability orders*

The implementation of sections 130 to 132 of the BSA brought into force Building Liability Orders. The BSA allows liability under the DPA for breach of Building Regulations or for other building safety matters, to be imputed to related companies by orders obtained from the High Court. A court can make a Building Liability Order if just and equitable to do so.

An order may be made providing that any "liability" of one corporate is also the liability of another if "associated". Liability arises under the DPA or as a result of building safety risk. An associate one that controls the other or another controls them both.

4.5.2 Remediation and Remediation Contribution Orders

Two new concepts came into effect: the Remediation Order (section 123) and the Remediation Contribution Order (section 124). These orders may compel relevant landlords to remedy specified defects that have arisen from construction or conversion work carried out within the period of 30 years up to 28 June 2022, and which cause a "building safety risk" (defined in s120 (5)), which includes risks to the safety of people "in and about" a building: from the spread of fire to the collapse of all, or part of a building.

4.6 Breach of Building Regulations and construction products

The BSA significantly changes the liability landscape in relation to the construction of both domestic and commercial new buildings. A general right of action for breach of the Building Regulations will be brought in force. Direct rights of action have also been introduced against construction product manufacturers in relation to domestic properties which are unfit for habitation.

4.6.1 General right of action for breach of Building Regulations

Section 38 of the Building Act 1984 was due to come into force on 28 June 2022, nearly 38 years later.

Section 38 provides a statutory right to claim compensation for physical damage (e.g. injury or damage to property) and/or mental trauma from those responsible, where such damage is caused by a breach of the Building Regulations.

4.6.2 Powers to sue construction products manufacturers

Under sections 147 to 155 of the BSA a damages claim, with effect from 28 June 2022, can be brought against a manufacturer of construction products whose breaches of the Construction Products Regulations 1991 cause a building or dwelling to become unfit for habitation.

4.7 Approved inspectors and architects

The BSA has removed the requirements relating to insurance for approved inspectors and strengthened the powers that the Architects Registration Board has under the Architects Act 1997.

4.7.1   Approved inspectors insurance

With effect from 28 July 2022, by the coming into force of section 48 of the BSA, the requirements relating to insurance for approved inspectors were removed from the Building Act 1984.

The Building (Approved Inspectors etc.) (Amendment) (England) Regulations 2022, which amended the Building (Approved Inspectors etc.) Regulations 2010, came into force on the same day.

4.7.2   Amendments to the Architects Act 1997

Sections 157 to 159 of the BSA, which came into force on 28 June 2022, amended the Architects Act 1997 to strengthen the powers that the Architects Registration Board has to measure and assess competence and increase transparency to members of the public procuring architectural services.

4.8   Regulations

Building and Construction Products Regulations have been amended.

4.8.1   The Building (Amendment) Regulations 2018

The Building (Amendment) Regulations 2018, which came into force on 21 December 2018, introduced new restrictions on the combustibility of materials contained within external walls of "relevant buildings" in England. "Relevant buildings" included residential and institutional buildings that were more than 18 m high.

Materials used within external walls of those buildings would need to be either Euro Class A2-s1, d0 or Euro Class A1. Other test standards or the use of terms such as "non-combustible" or "limited combustibility" would not guarantee compliance with these standards.

The restrictions were very extensive and included all materials contained within the external wall (not just insulation and cladding): for example, materials which passed through the wall, such as ducts and pipes.

The restrictions also applied to certain types of "specified attachments" which included balconies, solar shading and solar panels. A list of materials which were excluded from the restrictions included window frames, doors, seals, gaskets, electrical wiring and membranes (Fire Industry Association, 2019).

In addition, the Ministry of Housing, Communities & Levelling Up (2022) published "Guidance – Building (Amendment) Regulations 2018: frequently asked questions".

4.8.2   The Building etc. (Amendment) (England) Regulations 2022

The Building etc. (Amendment) (England) Regulations 2022, which came into force on 1 December 2022, amended the Combustible Materials Ban that was introduced in England in 2018 following the Grenfell Tower Fire. The changes will apply to new buildings and to existing buildings only where they are undergoing work. The regulations:

- ban the use of certain metal composite materials from use in the external walls and specified attachments of all buildings
- include within the scope of the Combustible Materials Ban elements of solar shading devices whose primary function is to provide shade or deflect sunlight
- amend the list of materials exempted from the Combustible Materials Ban to include fibre optic cables and insulation up to 300 mm from ground level
- update the "reaction to fire" classification that materials must meet to comply with the Combustible Materials Ban, to the current version of the British Standard
- reduce the height at which a building must comply with the relevant standard on external fire spread on walls where there is a material change of use of the building, from 15 to 11 m

The regulations also brought hotels, hostels and boarding houses which are more than 18 m in height within the scope of the Combustible Materials Ban.

4.8.3   The Construction Products (Amendment) Regulations 2022

The Construction Products (Amendment) Regulations 2022, which came into force on 20 July 2022, provided that the Secretary of State is an enforcement authority in relation to construction products in England, Wales, Scotland and Northern Ireland.

4.9   Fire safety

The Fire Safety Act 2021 and The Fire Safety (England) Regulations 2022 have come into force. The Regulatory Reform (Fire Safety) Order 2005 has been strengthened.

4.9.1   Fire Safety Act 2021

The Fire Safety Act 2021 (FSA) received Royal Assent on 29 April 2021 and commenced on 16 May 2022. The FSA amends the Regulatory Reform (Fire Safety) Order 2005 (the Fire Safety Order). The FSA applies to England and Wales.

The FSA clarifies the scope of the Fire Safety Order to make clear it applies to the structure, external walls (including cladding and balconies) and individual flat entrance doors between domestic premises and the common parts (Home Office, 2022a).

4.9.2   Regulatory Reform (Fire Safety) Order 2005 changes

Section 156 of the BSA introduced a number of measures to strengthen the Fire Safety Order. The level of fines for three specific offences has been increased, and a Responsible Person's failure to follow statutory guidance can be used as evidence of breach of the Fire Safety Order.

The other amendments place new requirements on Responsible Persons including duties to record relevant fire safety information. These new requirements will facilitate the identification of Responsible Persons and those appointed by Responsible Persons to carry out fire risk assessments, encourage Responsible Persons to cooperate and coordinate with one another, preserve essential fire safety information over a building's lifetime and work towards ensuring that a consistent approach is taken to fire safety by improving the quality of fire risk assessments and supporting enforcement action.

In all multi-occupied residential buildings, Responsible Persons for the common parts will also be required to provide residents with specific fire safety information that is comprehensible and relevant to them. In high-rise residential buildings where the Fire Safety Order and building safety regime will overlap, the cooperation duty placed on Responsible Persons will apply in respect of Accountable Persons to support a whole-system approach to safety in their building.

To further ensure the quality of fire risk assessments, a requirement will be placed on the Responsible Person to ensure any person they engage to undertake all or any part of the fire risk assessment is competent.

4.9.3   *The Fire Safety (England) Regulations 2022*

The Fire Safety (England) Regulations 2022 (the FS Regulations) have been introduced as an important step towards implementing the recommendations of the Grenfell Tower Inquiry Phase 1 report. The FS Regulations are being introduced under Article 24 of the Fire Safety Order and came into force on 23 January 2023. The FS Regulations apply to England only.

The FS Regulations introduce new duties under the Fire Safety Order for building owners or managers (Responsible Persons). The FS Regulations seek to improve the fire safety of blocks of flats in ways which are practical, cost-effective for individual leaseholders and proportionate to the risk of fire (Home Office, 2022b).

For high-rise residential buildings (a multi-occupied residential building at least 18 m in height or seven or more storeys), Responsible Persons must:

- share electronically with their local fire and rescue service (FRS) information about the building's external wall system and provide the FRS with electronic copies of floor plans and building plans for the building
- keep hard copies of the building's floor plans, in addition to a single-page orientation plan of the building, and the name and UK contact details of the Responsible Person in a secure information box which is accessible by firefighters
- install wayfinding signage in all high-rise buildings which is visible in low light conditions
- establish a minimum of monthly checks on lifts which are for the use of firefighters in high-rise residential buildings and on essential pieces of firefighting equipment

- inform the FRS if a lift used by firefighters or one of the pieces of firefighting equipment is out of order for longer than 24 hours

For multi-occupied residential buildings over 11 m in height, Responsible Persons must:

- undertake quarterly checks on all communal fire doors and annual checks on flat entrance doors

In all multi-occupied residential buildings, Responsible Persons must:

- provide residents with relevant fire safety instructions and information about the importance of fire doors.

References

Statutes

Architects Act 1997
Building Act 1984
Building Safety Act 2022
Defective Premises Act 1972
Fire Safety Act 2021

Secondary legislation

Regulatory Reform (Fire Safety) Order 2005
The Building (Amendment) Regulations 2018
The Building (Approved Inspectors etc.) (Amendment) (England) Regulations 2022
The Building (Approved Inspectors etc.) Regulations 2010
The Building etc. (Amendment) (England) Regulations 2022
The Building Safety Act 2022 (Commencement No. 1, Transitional and Saving Provisions) Regulations 2022
The Building Safety Act 2022 (Commencement No. 2) Regulations 2022
The Building Safety Act 2022 (Commencement No. 3 and Transitional Provision) Regulations 2022
The Building Safety (Leaseholder Protections) (England) Regulations 2022
The Building Safety (Leaseholder Protections) (Information etc.) (England) Regulations 2022
The Construction Products (Amendment) Regulations 2022
The Fire Safety (England) Regulations 2022

Cases

Rendlesham Estates v Barr Ltd [2014] EWHC 3968 (TCC)

Websites

DLUHC (2022) Guidance: The Building Safety Act, [online] Available from: https://www.gov.uk/guidance/the-building-safety-act (Accessed 31 October 2022).

Fire Industry Association (2019) Guide to the Building (Amendment) Regulations 2018, [online] Available from: https://www.labc.co.uk/sites/default/files/2019-03/EXT.FIA-Guide-to-the-building-%28amendments%29-regulations.V1.190319.pdf (Accessed 25 October 2022).

Home Office (2022a) Policy paper: Fire Safety Act 2021, [online] Available from: https://www.gov.uk/government/publications/fire-safety-act-2021 (Accessed 19 August 2022).

Home Office (2022b) Guidance: Fire Safety (England) Regulations 2022, [online] Available from: https://www.gov.uk/government/publications/fire-safety-england-regulations-2022 (Accessed 19 August 2022).

MHCLG (2021) Outline transition plan for the building safety bill, [online] Available from: https://www.gov.uk/government/publications/building-safety-bill-transition-plan/outline-transition-plan-for-the-building-safety-bill (Accessed 18 August 2022).

MHCLG (2022) Guidance – Building (Amendment) Regulations 2018: frequently asked questions, [online] Available from: https://www.gov.uk/government/publications/building-amendment-regulations-2018-frequently-asked-questions/building-amendment-regulations-2018-frequently-asked-questions (Accessed 25 October 2022).

5 Regulations

Nenpin Dimka

5.1 Introduction

The purpose of this chapter is to summarise the regulatory changes resulting from and following the Grenfell Tower fire. To begin, an overview of the historical background is presented along with the Building Act 1984. The Building Regulations 2010 are discussed, and links to the guidance documents, known as the Approved Documents (ADs), are established.

Guidance and compliance are distinguished with regard to the performance requirements of the ADs. This chapter then provides a comprehensive overview of the range of ADs. Regulatory changes and the purpose of amendments are highlighted, then a focus on Approved Document B (AD B), the guidance for fire safety. Amendments which have followed since the Grenfell disaster are outlined, including the ban on combustible materials and current amendments focusing on high-rise residential buildings.

5.2 Overview of Building Regulations

5.2.1 Historical background

In England, the first acts were rooted in the 17th century. In 1666, the Great Fire of London destroyed approximately 80% of the city, including about 13,000 houses. In the aftermath of the fire, an Act for rebuilding the City of London in 1667 was passed. Its purpose was to avert the re-occurrence of the disaster. Its coverage included maximum story heights to eliminate overcrowding and stipulations for houses to be constructed with brick or stone instead of timber. Compliance was enforced by the first building control surveyors known then as the City Viewers.

Similarly, in the late 19th century, as a consequence of problems with infectious diseases, the Public Health Act 1875 was passed in August of that year. Significantly local authorities were given new powers and established as urban and rural authorities. For London County Council area districts, surveyors were responsible, and for the rest of England, the local authorities. Although construction techniques at the time could be described as relatively straightforward, suitable plans still had to be submitted for local authority approval.

DOI: 10.1201/9781003357452-5

In the years following the First World War, the complexity of buildings only increased due to the widespread use of steel and the introduction of reinforced concrete. This added an additional layer to approvals of building design involving structural analysis, which was later included in the legislation. By the Second World War, there was a wide range of practice codes and British standard specifications to accommodate the growth of building technology.

Around this period, the "deemed to satisfy" provisions regarding the fitness of material were first introduced by the building by-laws of 1953. Under the Department of Public Health, in 1965, the first national building regulations were established. The Building Regulations 1965 include fire protection to structural elements, structural fire precautions, minimum stairway dimensions and requirements for partitions or compartment walls.

The Building Regulations 1972 were a metric reissue followed by The Building Regulations 1976. Until April 1980, there were no fees for the submission of plans; they were introduced under The Building (Prescribed Fees) Regulations 1980. Significant consolidations of nearly all previous building control legislation, including new proposals and streamlining the building regulations, came in the form of the Building Act 1984, which had its roots in the Government proposal written in a command paper in February 1981 – *the future of building control in England and Wales*. In 1985 the private option use of an Approved Inspector first appeared under The Building (Approved Inspector) Regulations 1985.

Despite retaining many elements of the 1976 Building Regulations, the 1985 Building Regulations had a new form and arrangement. Approved Documents B1: Means of escape have remained legally enforceable since this period, unlike other ADs that used different methods to achieve compliance.

In 1992, Building Regulations 1991 came into force on 1 June, and more than half of the Approved Documents were revised. Amendments in 1994 brought changes to specific regulations and requirements, including new ADs for Parts F: Ventilation and L: Conservation of fuel and power.

Several amendments have followed since 1995. Notable amongst these include The Building Regulations (Amendment No. 2) Regulations 1999 culminating in the 2000 editions of AD B; The consolidation of the Building Regulations 2010 and the Building (Approved Inspectors etc.) Regulations 2010. Nonetheless, compliance has always relied on the Regulations rather than the content of ADs – which are considered non-mandatory and purely as "practical guidance with respect to the requirements of any provision of building regulations" (section 6 of the Building Act 1984) (Table 5.1).

Table 5.1 Building Legislation within UK

Act	Regulations	Implementation
Building Act 1984	Building Regulations 2010	Approved Documents

5.2.2   Building Act 1984

The primary legislation is the Building Act 1984. The Act's prime purpose is to enable the conservation of fuel and power and prevent waste, consumption and contamination of water.

The Building Act 1984 has five parts:

Part 1 – The Building Regulations

Part 2 – Supervision of building work etc., other than by a local authority

Part 3 – Other provisions about buildings

Part 4 – General

Part 5 – Supplementary

Part 5 of the document contains seven schedules containing a list of the principal areas which require regulation. Also, to show how the building regulations (Part 1) are to be controlled by the local authorities. The schedules are:

Schedule 1 – Building Regulations

Schedule 2 – Relaxation of Building Regulations

Schedule 3 – Inner London

Schedule 4 – Provisions consequential upon public body's notice

Schedule 5 – Transitional provisions

Schedule 6 – Consequential amendments

Schedule 7 – Repeals

The principal area of materials and workmanship is covered in Regulation 7, stating:

a   *with adequate and proper materials, which:*

   i *are appropriate for the circumstances in which they are used*

   ii *are adequately mixed or prepared*

   iii *are applied, used or fixed so as adequately to perform for which they are designed*

b   *in a workmanlike manner.*

5.3   The Building Regulations 2010

5.3.1   Overview

The Building Regulations prescribe a minimum set of standards and basic performance for the design and construction of buildings to protect people's health, welfare and safety and minimise any waste or environmental damage. The national standards set out technical and procedural provisions that are mandatory for the design and construction of all new and altered building works.

To demonstrate compliance with the relevant Building Regulations, applications for building regulations approval include technical and procedural details, including construction methods, structural calculations, material specifications and the like.

The Regulations are supported by several general recommendations regarding specific aspects of the design and construction of buildings – commonly called the

"Approved Documents (ADs)". There are 15 technical categories which the ADs offer guidance towards achieving compliance.

These are:

Part A: Structure

Part B: Fire safety

Part C: Site preparation and resistance to moisture

Part D: Toxic substances

Part E: Resistance to the passage of sound

Part F: Ventilation

Part G: Sanitation, hot water and water efficiency

Part H: Drainage and waste disposal

Part J: Combustion appliances and fuel storage systems

Part K: Protection from falling, collision and impact

Part L: Conservation of fuel and power

Part M: Access to and use of buildings

Part N: Glazing safety

Part O: Overheating – New residential buildings

Part P: Electrical safety

Part Q: Security

Part R: Physical infrastructure for high speed electronic communication networks

Part S: Infrastructure for the charging of electric vehicles

Regulation 7: Material and workmanship

These are considered acceptable levels of safety and standards set out as *guidance.*

5.3.2 Compliance vs. guidance

In each AD, the actual requirements from the Building Regulations relevant to the subject area are reproduced. These are then followed by practical and technical guidance (with examples) showing how the requirements can be met in some common building situations. There may, however, be alternative ways of complying with the requirements to those shown in the ADs, and you are, therefore, under no obligation to adopt any particular solution contained in an AD if you prefer to meet the requirement(s) in another way.

ADs provide detailed and practical guidance on how to comply with building regulations. Therefore, adherence to the ADs is considered evidence of compliance with the Building Regulations. In other words, the government sets out building regulations as a legal requirement, and the ADs guide how to meet requirements for typical building situations and performance expectations.

Given the generic nature of the guidance documents, understanding the building regulatory system to ensure compliance must be contextualised according to the situation and the materials used.

As a result, there is an expectation of achieving compliance with requirements if the guidance of an AD is followed. However, this assumption cannot be regarded as definitive, and compliance cannot be guaranteed.

When building work is intended, proposals should be checked for compliance. Consultations with a Building Control Body (BCB) is advised. There are two possible choices of BCB: the Local Authority Building Control (LABC) or the Approved Inspector Building Control (AIBC). According to the Building Act 1984, they have the duty to ensure that the Building Regulations are adhered to when building works are carried out in their jurisdiction. This obligation is accomplished by making regular inspections of building works at certain stages of work.

However, this framework has been identified to have some ambiguity, particularly in the clarity of the guidance and the roles and responsibilities, which have been found to impact compliance and undermine achieving the primary role of protecting society and reducing environmental impact.

5.3.3   Procedure for changes (review and reform)

There is a constant need to amend building regulations in order to meet the growing demand for better, safer, accessible structures and reduced environmental damage – as well as harmonise with emerging international standards in some aspects.

Whenever there are common issues between one and more parties, necessary changes will be implemented following consultation with all parties involved. Similarly, if there are aspects considered to be deficient, for instance, as a result of the Grenfell Tower Inquiry, major revisions were made to AD B and Regulation 7.

There are currently 17 (parts) ADs as listed in Table 5.2.

Table 5.2 List of Approved Documents and Amendments

Section (Part)	Title	Edition	Latest Amendment
A	Structure	2004	2010 and 2013
B	Fire safety	2019	2022
	Volume 1: Dwellings	2019	2022
	Volume 2: Buildings other than dwellings		
C	Site preparation and resistance to moisture	2004	2013
D	Toxic substances	1992	2013
E	Resistance to the passage of Sound	2003	2015
F	Ventilation	2021	
	Volume 1: Dwellings		
	Volume 2: Buildings other than dwellings		
G	Sanitation, hot water safety and water efficiency	2015	2016
H	Drainage and waste disposal	2015	2015
J	Combustion appliances and fuel storage systems	2010	2013
K	Protection from falling, collision and impact	2013	
L	Conservation of fuel and power	2021	
	Volume 1: Dwellings	2021	
	Volume 2: Buildings other than dwellings		
M	Access to and use of buildings	2015	
	Volume 1: Dwellings	2015	
	Volume 2: Buildings other than dwellings		

(*Continued*)

Table 5.2 (Continued)

Section (Part)	Title	Edition	Latest Amendment
O	Overheating – New residential buildings	2021	
P	Electrical safety – Dwellings	2013	
Q	Security – Dwellings	2015	
R	Physical infrastructure for high-speed electronic communication networks	2016	
S	Infrastructure for the charging of electric vehicles	2021	
	Regulation 7 – Material and workmanship	2013	2018

5.4   Amendment to building regulations post-Grenfell

5.4.1   Combustible material ban

A ban on combustible cladding was introduced to the Building Regulations on 21st December 2018. It prohibits the use of combustible materials on external walls of high-rise buildings over 18 m, including new blocks of flats, hospitals, residential care premises and student accommodation.

A retrospective application of this rule was not applicable. Similarly, for buildings where the full plans were submitted, the work has been exempt. Therefore, the new rules will only apply to future new-build projects and not existing buildings or schemes that had already started by 21st February 2019.

As a result, only materials of Euroclass A2 or better can be used on the external facades of residential buildings between 11 m and 18 m in height. A number of combustible materials are prohibited by this standard, including plastics, timber cladding and high-pressure laminates.

Systems that have passed large-scale tests will allow the use of a wider range of combustible materials. Buildings exceeding 18 m are no longer eligible for this option. Consequently, certain combustible materials will be permitted in medium-rise buildings as part of tested systems, but metal composite material cladding panels with an unmodified polyethylene core (MCM PE) are banned on all buildings regardless of height.

Compared to the previous guidelines, the new measures represent a substantial tightening of existing guidance, which had no restrictions whatsoever on their use at this height.

5.4.2   Approved Document B: Fire Safety

In 1985 under the Department of the Environment a review of the Building Regulations led to significant changes in AD B in a number of key aspects. These areas reflected advances in construction technology and the adoption of guidance as opposed to mandatory rules for means of escape design.

A new requirement for fire service access was introduced, requirements for compartmentalisation were relaxed and consideration was placed on sprinklers with regard to periods of fire resistance. AD B is divided into two parts based on building types: one is for dwelling houses and the second for other buildings (non-dwellings).

Following the tragic event of the Grenfell Tower Fire, an independent review of Building Regulations, particularly those relating to fire safety, was launched by the UK Government. The findings gave rise to substantial amendments, which came into effect in 2019 and 2020.

The five aspects of fire safety in the construction of buildings impacted are as follows:

- Buildings shall have an appropriate means of early warning and escape in the event of a fire.
- The internal spread of fire should be inhibited within the building by ensuring internal linings (the products used to line ceilings, walls, etc.) adequately resist the spread of flame over their surface and have a rate of heat release, or fire growth, that is reasonable.
- In the event of a fire, the building's stability will be maintained for a reasonable period: walls common to two or more dwellings should adequately resist the spread of fire between those buildings.
- Fire spread should be inhibited in buildings which have been subdivided through the use of fire-resisting materials or fire suppression systems. The unseen spread of fire and smoke within concealed spaces in a building's structure is inhibited.
- The external walls and roof of a building are able to resist the spread of fire from one building to another. Buildings have reasonable access for fire appliances and facilities to assist firefighters in the protection of life.

5.4.3   *Approved Document B (new amendments)*

5.4.3.1   *Building safety: review and reforms*

Dame Judith Hackitt's recommendations instigated a review of the building safety prompted by the Grenfell Tower Fire. Below are highlights of significant stages of the revision:

- 6 June 2019–31 July 2019: consultation on proposals for reform of the building safety system: Building a safer future: proposals for reform of the building safety regulatory system
- 5 September 2019: the Secretary of State, Robert Jenrick, announced the establishment of "a new protection board" to increase fire protection inspections ahead of the new safety regime coming into force
- 1 October 2019–10 January 2020: the Future Homes Standard (relating to new home energy efficiency) a consultation
- 28 October 2019: Dame Judith Hackitt was announced to provide independent advice to the government on how best to establish the powerful new Building Safety Regulator

– Queen's Speech in December 2019: the government announced its intention to introduce a Building Safety Bill that would "Put in place new and enhanced regulatory regimes for building safety and construction products, ensuring residents have a stronger voice in the system".

5.4.3.2　*Approved Document B 2020 amendments*

There have been extensive changes made to both volumes of AD B, including the updating of the document format and the simplifying of its language. As a result, most sections have been revised (including numbering).

The amendments focused on the following fire safety requirements in blocks of flats:

– Sprinklers guidance consolidated to a new Appendix E
– A reduction in the trigger height from 30 m to 11 m
– Wayfinding signage for the fire service
– New recommendations for the identification of floors and flats within apartment buildings with 2 or more storeys above 11 m
– Purpose group number 2 is now included in reference to "residential" buildings in the guidance on boundaries
– The design of blocks of flats has moved from Volume 2 to Volume 1
– European fire classifications are provided within the main body of the document with transposition to a national classification provided in Appendix B
– The guidance on external stairs has been consolidated
– Fire safety information (under Regulation 38) has been moved from an appendix to a new section
– The guidance on insulating core panels has moved from an appendix to the wall and ceiling linings section
– The guidance on fire dampers and ventilation systems has been consolidated

5.4.3.3　*Approved Document B 2022 amendments*

The changes highlighted in this amendment took effect on 1 December 2022 for use in England.

The changes focus on the following fire safety provisions:

– Ban of combustible materials in and on the external walls of buildings:
　Consequential amendments following the laying of the Building (Amendment) (England) Regulations 2022
　Updated provisions in sections 10 and 12 of Volume 1 and 2, respectively, for residential buildings (purpose groups 1 and 2) with a storey 11 m or more in height
– Secure information boxes:
　A new recommendation for secure information boxes in blocks of flats with storeys over 11 m
– Evacuation alert systems:

A new recommendation for evacuation alert systems in blocks of flats with storeys over 18 m
- Clarifications and corrections:
Clarification of further diagrams, further text clarifications and corrections

The next section elaborates on some of the amendments listed above.

5.4.4 Current requirements for HRRB post-Grenfell

5.4.4.1 Requirement B1 means of warning and escape

5.4.4.1.1 SECTION 1: FIRE DETECTION AND ALARM SYSTEMS

- A fire detection and alarm system should be installed where a new habitable room is provided above or below the ground storey or at the ground storey, without a final exit.
- Smoke alarms should be provided in the circulation spaces of the dwelling.

5.4.4.1.2 SECTION 2: MEANS OF ESCAPE – FLATS

- Where a flat is accessed via the common parts of a block of flats it may be necessary to provide a protected entrance hall to meet the provisions of the protected lobby or protected corridor (minimum REI 30) with a minimum 0.4 m² of permanent ventilation or be protected from the ingress of smoke by a mechanical smoke control system.
- Provide a protected stairway plus a sprinkler system in accordance with Appendix E: Sprinklers and smoke alarms provided in accordance with section 1: Fire detection and alarm system.
- *Lighting of common escape routes* for two-storey blocks of flats exempt from providing, all escape routes should have adequate artificial lighting. If the mains electricity power supply fails, escape lighting should illuminate the route (including external escape routes).
- *Smoke control of common escape routes by natural smoke ventilation*: Can now be the smoke shaft should be constructed from a class A1 material. All vents should be a smoke leakage (Sa) rated fire doorset.
- *Enclosure of common stairs:* every common stair should be a protected stairway. Where the protected stairway passes from one compartment to another, it should be within a protected shaft.

5.4.4.2 Requirement B3 internal fire spread (structure)

5.4.4.2.1 SECTION 7: COMPARTMENTATION/SPRINKLERS – FLATS

- All of the following should be provided as compartment walls and compartment floors and should have, as a minimum, the fire resistance given in Appendix B, Table B3.

a   Any floor (unless it is within a flat, i.e. between one storey and another within one individual dwelling)
b   Any wall separating a flat from another part of the building
c   Any wall enclosing a refuse storage chamber
d   Any wall common to two or more buildings

5.4.4.2.2   SECTION 9: PROTECTION OF OPENINGS AND FIRE-STOPPING

– Every joint, imperfect fit and opening for services through a fire-separating element should be sealed with fire-stopping to ensure that the fire resistance of the element is not impaired. Fire-stopping delays the spread of fire and, generally, the spread of smoke as well.
– If air handling ducts pass through fire-separating elements, the fire performance of the elements should be maintained using one or more of the following four methods. In most ductwork systems, a combination of the four methods is best.
a   Method 1 – thermally activated fire dampers
b   Method 2 – fire-resisting enclosures
c   Method 3 – protection using fire-resisting ductwork
d   Method 4 – automatically activated fire and smoke dampers triggered by smoke detectors

5.4.4.3   *Requirement B4 external fire spread and requirement B5: access and facilities for the fire service*

5.4.4.3.1   REGULATION 7 – MATERIALS AND WORKMANSHIP

– Building work shall be carried out so that relevant metal composite material does not become part of an external wall, or specified attachment, of any building.
– Subject to stated conditions, building work shall be carried out so that materials which become part of an external wall, or specified attachment, of a relevant building are of European Classification A2-s1, d0 or A1 (classified in accordance with the reaction to fire classification). Conditions include:
– insulation and waterproofing materials used below ground level or up to 300 mm above that level
– materials which form the top horizontal floor layer of a balcony are of European Classification A1fl or A2fl-sl (classified in accordance with the reaction to fire classification), provided that the entire layer has an imperforate substrate under it

5.4.4.3.2   SECTION 10: RESISTING FIRE SPREAD OVER EXTERNAL WALLS

5.4.4.3.2.1   Materials and products

– In buildings that include a "residential" purpose (purpose groups 1 and 2) with a storey 11 m or more in height any insulation products, filler materials (such as the core materials of metal composite panels, sandwich panels and window spandrel panels but not including gaskets, sealants and similar), etc. used in the construction of an external wall should be class A2-s1, d0 or better. This restriction does not apply to masonry cavity wall construction, which complies with in section 8. Where Regulation 7(2) applies, that regulation prevails over all the provisions in this paragraph.

5.4.4.3.2.2 Balconies

– In buildings that include a "residential" purpose (purpose groups 1 and 2) with a storey 11 m or more in height (see Diagram D6 in Appendix D) balconies should meet either of the following conditions.
   a Only contain materials achieving class A1 or A2-s1, d0, except for any of the following:
      i Cavity trays when used between two leaves of masonry
      ii Intumescent and fire-stopping materials where the inclusion of the materials is necessary to meet the requirements of Part B of Schedule 1 to the Building Regulations 2010
      iii Membranes
      iv Seals, gaskets, fixings, sealants and backer rods
      v Thermal break materials where the inclusion of the materials is necessary to meet the thermal bridging requirements of Part L of Schedule 1 to the Building Regulations 2010
      vi Any material achieving class A1fl or A2fl-s1 when it forms the top horizontal floor layer of a balcony and is provided with an imperforate substrate under it which extends to the full size of the class A1fl or A2fl-s1 material
      vii Electrical installations
      viii Fibre optic cables
   b Achieve both of the following conditions:
      i Have an imperforate soffit which extends to the full area of the balcony, achieves a minimum REI 30 rating and is constructed of materials achieving class A2-s1, d0 or better.
      ii Materials achieving class B-s1, d0 or worse extending beyond the boundary of a single compartment should include a band of material rated class A2-s1, d0 or better, a minimum of 300 mm in width centred on that boundary line. Where regulation 7(2) applies, that regulation prevails over all the provisions in this paragraph.

5.4.4.3.2.3 Metal composite materials

– Regulation 7(1A) prohibits the use of relevant metal composite materials in the external walls of all buildings of any height. Relevant metal composite materials are defined (in regulation 2(6)(c)) as any panel or sheet having a thickness of no more than 10 mm which is composed of a number of layers, two or more of which are made of metal, alloy or metal compound and one or more of which is a substantial layer made of a material having a gross calorific value of more than 35 MJ/kg when tested in accordance with BS EN ISO 1716. A substantial layer is defined as a layer which is at least 1 mm thick or has a mass per unit area of at least 1 kg/m².

– Membranes used as part of the external wall construction above ground level should achieve a minimum of class B-s3, d0. Roofing membranes do not need to achieve a minimum of class A2-s1, d0 when used as part of a roof connecting to an external wall.

5.4.4.3.2.4   Additional considerations

– Membranes used as part of the external wall construction above ground level should achieve a minimum of class B-s3, d0. Roofing membranes do not need to achieve a minimum of class A2-s1, d0 when used as part of a roof connecting to an external wall.
– Any material achieving class A1fl or A2fl-s1 in accordance with BS EN 13501-1 is exempted when it meets both of the following conditions:
  i It forms the top horizontal floor layer of a balcony.
  ii It is provided with an imperforate substrate under it, which extends to the full size of the class A1fl or A2fl-s1 material.

5.4.4.4   *Requirement B5: Access and facilities for the fire service*

5.4.4.4.1   SECTION 15: ACCESS TO BUILDINGS FOR FIREFIGHTING PERSONNEL – FLATS

– The intention is to provide A facility to store building information for firefighters to complete their tasks.
– For dwellinghouses, access for a pumping appliance should be provided to within 45 m of all points inside the dwellinghouse. Every elevation to which vehicle access is provided should have a suitable door(s), not less than 750 mm wide, giving access to the interior of the building.
– For flats, either of the following provisions should be made:
  a Provide access for a pumping appliance to within 45 m of all points inside each flat of a block, measured along the route of the hose. Every elevation to which vehicle access is provided should have a suitable door(s), not less than 750 mm wide, giving access to the interior of the building. Door(s) should be provided such that there is no more than 60 m between each door and/or the end of that elevation (e.g. a 150 m elevation would need at least two doors).
– In buildings where a firefighting shaft is required, a minimum of two firefighting shafts should be provided in either of the following situations:
  a A building that has both of the following:
    i A storey with a floor area of 900 m² or more
    ii A storey 18 m or more above the fire and rescue service vehicle access level
  b A building with a basement storey which is more than 900 m²

5.4.4.4.2 EVACUATION ALERT SYSTEMS

– In blocks of flats (purpose group 1(a)) with a top storey over 18 m above ground level (see Diagram D6 in Appendix D), an evacuation alert system should be provided in accordance with BS 8629.

5.4.4.4.3 SECURE INFORMATION BOXES

– A secure information box provides a secure facility to store information about a building for use by the fire service during an incident.
– Blocks of flats (purpose group 1(a)) with a top storey more than 11 m above ground level (see Diagram D6 in Appendix D) should be provided with a secure information box.
– Consideration should also be given to other buildings with large, complex or uncommon layouts where the provision of a secure information box may be beneficial.
– The box should meet all of the following conditions:
  a Sized to accommodate all necessary information
  b Easily located and identified by firefighters
  c Secured to resist unauthorised access but readily accessible by firefighters
– Best practice guidance can be found in sections 2 to 4 of the Code of Practice for the Provision of Premises Information Boxes in Residential Buildings published by the Fire Industry Association (FIA).

Bibliography

HM Government (2022a) Amendments to the Approved Documents, [online] Available from: https://assets.publishing.service.gov.uk/government/uploads/system/uploads/attachment_data/file/1080214/ADB_amendment_booklet_June_2022.pdf (Accessed 30 January 2023).

HM Government (2022b) Approved Document B : Fire Safety 2019 edition incorporating 2020 and 2022 amendments, [online] Available from: https://assets.publishing.service.gov.uk/government/uploads/system/uploads/attachment_data/file/1124733/Approved_Document_B__fire_safety__volume_1_-_Dwellings__2019_edition_incorporating_2020_and_2022_amendments.pdf (Accessed 30 January 2023).

HM Government (2018) Review of the ban on combustible materials – GOV.UK, [online] Available from: https://www.gov.uk/guidance/ban-on-combustible-materials (Accessed 30 January 2023).

HM Government (2023a) Legislation.gov.uk, [online] Available from: https://www.legislation.gov.uk/ (Accessed 30 January 2023).

HM Government (2023b) The Building (Scotland) Regulations 2004, [online] Available from: https://www.legislation.gov.uk/ssi/2004/406/schedule/5/paragraph/2.7/2022-06-01 (Accessed 29 January 2023).

IH Reporters (2019) Insight – Grenfell Tower Inquiry report: full coverage, [online] Available from: https://www.insidehousing.co.uk/insight/insight/grenfell-tower-inquiry-report-full-coverage-63942 (Accessed 30 January 2023).

MHCLG (2020) Review of the ban on the use of combustible materials in and on the external walls of buildings, [online] Available from: https://www.gov.uk/government/

consultations/review-of-the-ban-on-the-use-of-combustible-materials-in-and-on-the-external-walls-of-buildings (Accessed 30 January 2023).

Peter, A. and Heath, L. (2022) Partial ban for combustible materials on new medium-rise buildings to be imposed, 1st June, [online] Available from: https://www.insidehousing.co.uk/news/news/partial-ban-for-combustible-materials-on-new-medium-rise-buildings-to-be-imposed-75931 (Accessed 30 January 2023).

Polley, S. (2014) Understanding the Building Regulations, Routledge, [online] Available from: https://www.routledge.com/Understanding-the-Building-Regulations/Polley/p/book/9780415717427 (Accessed 30 January 2023).

Potton, E. (2019) Building regulations and safety: review and reforms, [online] Available from: https://commonslibrary.parliament.uk/research-briefings/cbp-8482/ (Accessed 30 January 2023).

Tricker, R. and Alford, S. (2023) Building regulations in brief, [online] Available from: https://www.routledge.com/Building-Regulations-in-Brief/Tricker-Alford/p/book/9780367774233 (Accessed 30 January 2023).

6 Regulators

Jennifer Charlson

6.1 Introduction

The Building Safety Act (BSA) 2022 created three new bodies to provide an effective oversight of the new regime: the Building Safety Regulator (BSR), the National Regulator of Construction Products and the New Homes Ombudsman. The BSA included the introduction of a new regime of regulatory measures for high-rise residential and other in scope buildings.

The BSR was established under the Health and Safety Executive (HSE) in June 2022 and is due to become operational in April 2023. The BSR has a duty to establish and maintain three committees: Residents' Panel, Industry Competence Committee and Building Advisory Committee. The BSR must prepare a strategic plan and may subsequently prepare revised strategic plans, which must be submitted to the Secretary of State for approval.

The BSA also introduced new duties for "higher-risk buildings" during the occupation phase of a building. The higher-risk buildings in scope are over 18 m or 7 or more storeys and contain at least 2 residential units. Between October 2023 and October 2028, all existing buildings will come into the scope of the regulations.

The BSA has inserted a new Part 2A "Regulation of the Building Control Profession" into the Building Act 1984. Registration will open in October 2023 with the sections of the BSA related to registration coming into force in April 2024.

Local authorities have a statutory duty to ensure compliance with all building regulations (in particular, the Building Regulations 2010). It is generally the position that building control cannot be held responsible for signing off on defective plans. Those undertaking building work can choose between a local authority and a private sector Approved Inspector to oversee the works from a building control perspective.

The BSR will regulate developments through a series of three gateways. Permission from the BSR will be required before a development can proceed through each gateway. Gateway 1, which governs the planning stage, is already in force. From October 2023, developers will also have to pass through gateway 2 prior to the start of building work and gateway 3 upon the works' completion.

Occupational phase building safety duties are shared between three dutyholders: the Principal Accountable Person, Responsible Person and Accountable Person.

DOI: 10.1201/9781003357452-6

The Landlord is required to comply with the BSA and cooperate with other dutyholders. A tenant, who owns a residential unit or is a resident and over 16, must permit access for building safety purposes. The Accountable Person will need to apply for a Building Assessment Certificate to verify that they are meeting their prescribed duties. Accountable Persons (under the BSA) and Responsible Persons (under the Regulatory Reform (Fire Safety) Order 2005) will be required to cooperate with one another.

The New Homes Ombudsman Service (NHOS), introduced by the BSA, is to resolve disputes concerning new build homes. The BSA also enables social housing complainants to escalate a complaint directly to the Housing Ombudsman service once they have completed their landlord's complaints process.

The BSA introduced a freestanding cause of action against construction product manufacturers which cannot be excluded by contract. New requirements for products that are "safety critical", where their failure could cause death or serious injury to people, are to be introduced. The National Regulator for Construction Products (NRCP) will become fully operational once secondary legislation has been approved by Parliament.

6.2   Building Safety Act 2022

The BSA created three new bodies to provide an effective oversight of the new regime: the BSR, the National Regulator of Construction Products and the New Homes Ombudsman. The BSA included the introduction of a new regime of regulatory measures for high-rise residential and other in scope buildings.

6.2.1   *Regulators*

The BSR will oversee the safety and performance of all buildings, as well as having a special focus on high-rise buildings. It will promote competence and organisational capability within the sector including for building control professionals and tradespeople.

The NRCP will oversee a more effective construction products regulatory regime and lead and coordinate market surveillance and enforcement in this sector across the UK. The NRCP has already started taking enforcement action under the scope of existing regulations. The new regulatory regime will start to apply once the necessary secondary legislation on the future regulatory regime has been approved by Parliament.

The New Homes Ombudsman Scheme will allow relevant owners of new-build homes to escalate complaints to a New Homes Ombudsman. Developers of new-build homes will be required by secondary legislation to become and remain a member of the New Homes Ombudsman Scheme, and secondary legislation will also set out the enforcement framework and sanctions for breaching requirements. The Secretary of State may also approve or issue a developers' code of practice which sets out the standards of conduct and the standards of quality of work expected of the New Homes Ombudsman scheme's members.

6.2.2 Regulatory measures

The Building Safety Bill, as explained in July 2021, included the introduction of a new regime of regulatory measures for high-rise residential and other in scope buildings (MHCLG, 2021).

- Dutyholders having clear accountability and statutory responsibilities as buildings are designed, constructed and refurbished.
- Gateways (stop/go decision points) which will provide rigorous assessment of regulatory requirements to ensure building safety and regulatory compliance is considered at each stage of a building's design and construction.
- The requirement for a golden thread of building information – created, stored and updated throughout the building's lifecycle.
- Mandatory reporting to the new BSR of prescribed fire and structural safety occurrences.
- BSR oversight of building work as the building control body for high-rise residential and other in scope buildings will strengthen regulatory oversight and require dutyholders to implement appropriate measures to manage building regulations compliance.
- An ongoing duty on the Accountable Person for each high-rise residential building is to assess the building safety risk relating to the parts of the building for which they are responsible, take all reasonable steps to prevent a building safety risk materialising and limit any consequences to the safety of people in or around the building.

6.3   Building Safety Regulator

The BSR was established under the Health and Safety Executive on 28 June 2022. The BSR is due to become operational in April 2023.

Under section 3(1) of the BSA, the BSR is required to exercise its building functions with a view to:

a securing the safety of people in or about buildings in relation to risks arising from buildings; and
b improving the standard of buildings"

6.3.1 BSR main functions

The BSR has three main functions:

1 Overseeing the safety and performance system for all buildings. This will include advising Ministers on changes to building regulations, using data and research to identify emerging risks and managing the performance of building control bodies who inspect building work
2 Assisting and encouraging the improvement of competence in the built environment industry and amongst building control professionals

3 Leading implementation of the new, more stringent regulatory regime for higher-risk buildings

The BSR will have/has a range of effective enforcement powers in relation to high-rise residential buildings.

6.3.2   *BSR committees*

The BSR has a duty to establish and maintain three committees (H SE, 2022a):

- Residents' Panel: The purpose of the panel is to ensure that residents have a voice in the work of the BSR and are consulted on resident engagement, how residents escalate safety concerns to the regulator, the regulator's strategic plan and other matters that directly impact them.
- Industry Competence Committee: This will monitor industry competence and facilitate its improvement, publish guidance on industry competence and provide advice to the BSR and industry on competence.
- Building Advisory Committee (BAC): The Committee will help the BSR meet its duty to keep the safety and standard of all buildings under review by providing advice and expertise and helping in the development of future building regulations. The BAC held its inaugural meeting on 19 December 2022 (HSE, 2022b).

6.3.3   *BSR strategic plan and powers*

The BSR must prepare a strategic plan and may subsequently prepare revised strategic plans. These plans must be submitted to the Secretary of State for approval (sections 17 and 18 of the BSA).

The BSR should exercise its powers in line with regulatory best practice, taking a consistent and proportionate approach and targeting its enforcement activity at cases where action is needed.

6.4   Higher-risk buildings

The BSA also introduces new duties for "higher-risk buildings" during the occupation phase of a building. The higher-risk buildings in scope are over 18 m or 7 or more storeys and contain at least 2 residential units. It includes multi-occupied residential buildings, mixed use buildings with a residential element, student accommodation and educational accommodation. The design and construction phases of hospitals and care homes are also within scope.

Over time, however, the scope is likely to expand to include other buildings where people sleep and buildings of lower height. Between October 2023 and October 2028, all existing buildings will come into the scope of the regulations.

6.4.1   *Duties*

The duties are set out in Part 4 of the BSA, and they must be fulfilled by either the Principal Accountable Person, Accountable Person, or residents. The provisions of Part 4 of the BSA are not currently all in force.

The provisions concerning the meaning of "building safety risk" and "higher-risk building" are in force. However, the provisions which relate to the meaning of "Accountable Person" and other key definitions, registration and certificates, duties relating to building safety risks, duties relating to information and documents, engagement with residents, resident duties, enforcement, special measures and appeals are due to come into force on such day as the Secretary of State may by regulations appoint.

6.4.2 *Higher-risk buildings Accountable Person*

All occupied higher-risk buildings will have one clearly identifiable Accountable Person. All occupied "higher-risk buildings" must be registered with the BSR by October 2023. It is a criminal offence if a building is occupied but not registered after this date. This will allow the BSR to compile the national register of high-rise residential buildings in England, which will be made publicly available.

The Accountable Person for a building will be required to meet a range of duties to ensure resident safety, including conducting an assessment of building safety risks, taking proportionate steps to reduce and manage risks, summarising these in a safety case report for the building and storing information in the golden thread. The Accountable Person will also need to establish a residents' engagement strategy and complaints procedure.

The BSR will enforce the new, more stringent regulatory regime for higher-risk buildings, overseeing compliance with the new regulations once they come into force.

6.5 Regulation of the Building Control Profession

Section 42 of the BSA has inserted a new Part 2A "Regulation of the Building Control Profession" (sections 58A to 58Z10) into the Building Act 1984.

6.5.1 *Registration and conduct*

These provisions include that the BSR must:

- establish and maintain a register of building inspectors and building control approvers
- prepare and publish a code of conduct for registered building inspectors and professional conduct rules for building control approvers

6.5.2 *Investigation and discipline*

The provisions include that the BSR may:

- investigate a matter if it appears (on receipt of a complaint or otherwise) that a registered building inspector may be guilty of professional misconduct
- suspend the individual under investigation

- make one or more disciplinary orders, if, following an investigation, the BSR determines that an individual who is a registered building inspector is guilty of professional misconduct

6.5.3   *Offences*

A registered building inspector commits an offence if, with intent to deceive, they do anything which implies that work which is outside the scope of their registration is within the scope of their registration. The offence is punishable by a fine.

6.5.4   *Rules, reporting, investigations and inspection*

The provisions include that the BSR may:

- make rules ("operational standards rules") applying to local authorities and registered building control approvers in relation to their exercise of building control functions
- direct local authorities and registered building control approvers to provide it with reports, returns and other information relating to the exercise of their building control functions
- investigate the matter, if it appears (on receipt of a complaint or otherwise) that a local authority or registered building control approver may have contravened the operational standards rules
- give an improvement notice to a local authority or a registered building control approver if it appears (following an investigation) that the local authority or registered building control approver has contravened operational standards rules
- give a serious contravention notice to a local authority or a registered building control approver
- cancel a building control approver's registration
- recommend to the Secretary of State that the Secretary of State make an order to transfer functions to the Secretary of State or another local authority
- carry out an inspection of a local authority, or a registered building control approver, in relation to their exercise of building control functions

Registration will open in October 2023 with the sections of the BSA related to registration coming into force in April 2024.

6.6   Building control and duty of care

Local authorities have a statutory duty to ensure all building regulations (in particular, the Building Regulations 2010) are complied with; building control is shorthand for this enforcement role as well as a physical department of local authorities.

Since 1985, parts of building control have been privatised. Those undertaking building work can choose between (1) a local authority and (2) a private sector approved inspector (Approved Inspector) to oversee the works from a building control perspective.

An Approved Inspector is a person who, under section 49(1)(b) of the Building Act 1984 and in accordance with Regulation 5 of the Building (Approved Inspectors etc) Regulations 2010, is approved by the Construction Industry Council (CIC).

A duty of care is owed when there is reasonable foreseeability of loss, sufficient proximity of relationship and where it would be fair, just and reasonable to impose a duty. When considering whether it is fair, just and reasonable to impose a duty of care on public authorities, the courts take a restrictive approach.

It is generally the position that building control cannot be held responsible for signing off on defective plans. Reasons for this include:

- the absence of a contractual relationship between the party which has suffered loss and building control (in circumstances where the local authority is carrying out the building control function)
- there are no statutory provisions imposing liability on building control
- the decision in the House of Lords decision *Murphy v Brentwood District Council* [1991] UKHL 2

6.6.1 *Murphy v Brentwood*

In *Murphy v Brentwood*, the claimant purchased a property which transpired to be built on defective foundations. The claimant sought damages from Brentwood District Council's building control function in respect of diminution of property value, alleging that building control had negligently signed off on the foundation plans.

It was held that building control was not liable for the cost of remedying the defects. This was decided on the basis that for policy reasons, the common law duty to take reasonable care does not apply to building control in circumstances where no physical injury had been suffered and the loss is purely economic.

Therefore, according to *Murphy v Brentwood*, in most circumstances there is no legal recourse in respect of pure economic loss against building control which has approved defective plans.

6.7 Regulating construction

There will be extensive obligations in relation to notifying changes to the design to the BSR, and, for certain more significant changes, approval will need to be sought before works can proceed. These issues all have the potential to cause significant delays to the works and drive up construction cost.

Therefore, detailed design needs to be undertaken early as it will become harder to change fundamental design elements later in the process.

The BSR will regulate developments through a series of three gateways. Permission from the BSR will be required before a development can proceed through each gateway. Gateway 1, which governs the planning stage, is already in force.

From October 2023, developers will also have to pass through gateway 2 prior to the start of building work and gateway 3 upon the works' completion.

6.7.1   Gateway 1

Planning application stage approvals are referred to as Gateway 1 and have been introduced via amendments to secondary planning legislation.

Gateway 1 helps to ensure that applicants and decision-makers consider fire safety issues relevant to planning such as site layout, water supplies for firefighting purposes and access for fire appliances. Gateway 1 brings forward thinking on fire safety matters, as they relate to land use planning, to the earliest possible stage in the development process by requiring a fire statement with relevant applications for planning permission for development.

Gateway 1 came into force on 1 August 2021 through the introduction of the Town and Country Planning (Development Management Procedure and Section 62A Applications) (England) (Amendment) Order 2021.

From October 2023, developers will also have to pass through Gateway 2 prior to the start of building work and Gateway 3 upon the works' completion.

6.7.2   Gateway 2

Gateway 2 will replace the building control deposit of plans stage, before building work starts, with the BSR as the building control body for high-rise residential and other in-scope buildings. The government's guidance says that this will be a stop/go point or "hard stop".

Gateway 2 applies prior to commencement of building work and requires the BSR to be satisfied that designs and construction proposals satisfy the requirements of the Building Regulations and the BSA including information about how the new dutyholder, competence, "golden thread" and mandatory occurrence reporting requirements will be met.

In order to pass Gateway 2, the developer should make an application submitting:

- Full plans
- Safety critical products
- Fire strategy
- Fire and emergency file
- Construction control plan

The BSR has 12 weeks for Gateway 2 approval. In practice, the design should be fixed at this point as evidenced by the "golden thread".

If the BSR does not approve within the 12-week time limit, absent an agreed extension, the applicant has six weeks to apply directly to the Secretary of State under s.30A of the Building Act (a new provision not yet in force). If this does not happen, the proposal is that the approval application is deemed to have been rejected.

An applicant must give at least five days' notice to commence work. It is also indicated that if an application is approved, the BSR will agree a bespoke inspection schedule with the applicant and the BSR will need to be notified at these stages for inspection to take place.

6.7.3 Golden thread

The rationale for adopting a "golden thread" approach is to ensure that the design and as-built condition is clear and documented for the building owners, asset managers and forward purchasers. The "golden thread" should be developed over the lifetime of the building by the relevant dutyholders and Accountable Persons. Implementation can be by the use of digital technology: for example, Building information modelling (BIM).

The Code of practice: Digital management of fire safety information – Design, construction, handover, asset management and emergency response (BS 8644-1:2022) (BSI, 2022) was published on 31 July 2022. This code enables a common industry approach to the management of digital asset information in the built environment, particularly fire safety information.

6.7.4 During construction

Subsequently, a change control log should be maintained. Notifiable changes require 14-day notice. Major changes need an application to the BSR who has six weeks to approve the change.

The requirement for approval of a "major change" is intended to be another "hard stop", and work will not be able to continue until approval is received. If the BSR does not approve within the required six week period, the applicant may again apply under s.30A of the Building Act.

Certain more minor changes, referred to as "notifiable changes", will also require approval, but a shorter approval period of ten business days will apply. A list of such changes is set out in the consultation paper. Approval for these changes will not be a "hard stop", and the change can be made once the ten business day period has elapsed without any objection being received from the BSR.

It is expected now that the BSR will carry out inspections at the agreed stages but inspections could also be carried out without notice.

6.7.5 Gateway 3

Gateway 3 applies when building work is complete and requires the BSR to be satisfied that the works as built comply with the Building Regulations and that the finished building is safe to occupy. Government's guidance says that this will also be a "hard stop" i.e. building control approval must be obtained from the BSR before registering and commencing occupation of a higher-risk building. Once gateway 3 has been passed, the BSR will issue a completion certificate.

The BSR has 12 weeks to determine an application for a completion certificate/statement once provided with:

- As built details evidenced by the "golden thread"
- Client statement of compliance with Building Regulations
- Principal designer and principal contractor confirmation that they have discharged their construction-phase building safety duties.

It is now clear that a gateway 3 application can only be made once completion is achieved and full as-built plans will need to be submitted with the application. If the BSR does not approve within the 12-week time limit, then the s.30A of the Building Act procedure applies.

The information must also be handed over to the building owner to help them manage building safety risks when the building is in use by ensuring they have accurate, good quality, and up-to-date information. Once gateway 3 has been passed, the Accountable Person can register the building for occupation.

The BSA makes it a criminal offence for a building to be occupied prior to this completion certificate being issued.

6.8 Occupational phase

6.8.1 Building safety duties

Occupational phase building safety duties are shared between three dutyholders: the Principal Accountable Person, Responsible Person and Accountable Person.

Principal Accountable Person duties include the following:

- Registration of building
- Applying for the Building Assessment Certificate
- Assessing building safety risks and preparing safety case report
- Resident engagement strategy, mandatory occurrence reporting and complaints procedure

6.8.2 Building safety manager?

The building safety manager role was removed from the legislation as it made its way through the House of Lords. For occupied buildings, duties will fall to the Principal Accountable Person or Accountable Persons. In many buildings, however, the Principal Accountable Person is still likely to need someone to help them comply with their duties. In practice, the role is likely to be required to:

- day-to-day manage the safety and engagement with the residents
- manage the building in line with the safety case
- be the nominated individual with responsibility for the building

6.8.3 Residents' voice

The Accountable Person in a high-rise residential building will in future have duties to:

- Provide residents with information they need to understand safety measures in their building, who is accountable and how to report safety concerns
- Develop and implement a residents' engagement strategy, setting out how they will promote engagement with residents on building safety decisions and how residents can get involved
- Establish and operate a complaints procedure for residents to raise safety concerns

In future, residents will also be able to escalate their safety concerns to the BSR who will establish and operate a complaints procedure to handle residents' concerns

Residents will have clear legal obligations to comply with a reasonable request made by the Accountable Persons for information in connection with fulfilling one or more of their duties to assess safety risks in the building; to avoid actions that could pose a significant risk to the fire and structural safety of the building and to refrain from interfering with safety items in and around the building.

Where a resident fails to comply with their responsibilities, the Accountable Person may issue a contravention notice requesting that the resident remedies the contravention within a reasonable time. As a last resort, an Accountable Person will be able to go to the civil courts to enforce those responsibilities.

6.8.4 Landlord and tenant responsibilities

The Landlord is required to comply with the BSA and cooperate with other dutyholders. A tenant, who owns a residential unit or is a resident and over 16, must permit access for building safety purposes.

Residents of higher-risk buildings will also have building safety duties. Where they pay service charges, this will include the cost of measures required for the Principal Accountable Person to comply with the regulations in the BSA.

6.8.5 Building Assessment Certificate

The Accountable Person will need to apply for a Building Assessment Certificate to verify that they are meeting their prescribed duties. After the building is registered, the BSR will issue a call-in notification to the Accountable Person, directing them to apply for the Building Assessment Certificate, which they must do within 28 days.

To secure their certificate, the Accountable Person will submit the safety case report and other prescribed information to the BSR to satisfy them that they are meeting their duties. The circumstances under which an Accountable Person can expect to be called for certification will be set out in the BSR's strategic plan.

The following information will be need to compile that safety case report:

- Basic building information
- Building construction
- Resident profile
- Refurbishment
- Fire prevention and protection measures
- Structural safety
- Services and utilities
- Maintenance and inspection

Missing information may be obtained from the following sources:

- Archives
- Planning authority record
- Building control records
- Previous owners
- Supply chain
- Surveys/reports "which are proportionate"

The BSR will publish case studies and examples.

6.8.6   *Building and fire safety cooperation*

Accountable Persons (under the BSA) and Responsible Persons (under the Regulatory Reform (Fire Safety) Order 2005) will be required to cooperate with one another when fulfilling their duties to deliver a holistic approach to the management of building and fire safety risks in their building.

The BSA makes provision for the Accountable Person to recover the costs in meeting their enhanced obligations under the new regime. These provisions (the Building Safety Charge) will be commenced prior to the occupation duties.

6.8.7   *Strengthening enforcement*

In addition to the financial and reputational risks of not passing through the gateways or not receiving a Building Assessment Certificate, the BSA:

- creates new imprisonable criminal offences to ensure that those responsible for the safety of high-rise residential buildings comply with their responsibilities – including making directors and managers of companies personally liable
- ensures that the Accountable Person applies to register the building with the BSR and that they apply for the Building Assessment Certificate when directed to do so by the regulator, with failure to do so in both cases a criminal offence
- ensures that if a dutyholder fails to meet requirements, the BSR can issue a compliance notice to ensure issues are rectified by a set date, with failure to do so a criminal offence

- ensures where there are serious failings, enabling the BSR to trigger "special measures" provisions on application to the First-tier Tribunal, whereby a Special Measures Manager is appointed with extensive powers over the management of the building.

The BSR will be able to appoint "authorised officers" to exercise investigatory powers on its behalf, and obstructing or impersonating such an officer will be an offence, as will be failing to provide information when required or providing false or misleading information.

6.9   Ombudsmen

The NHOS, introduced by the BSA, is to resolve disputes concerning new build homes. The BSA also enables social housing complainants to escalate a complaint directly to the Housing Ombudsman service, once they have completed their landlord's complaints process.

6.9.1   *New Homes Ombudsman Service*

Schedule 9 of the BSA introduced provision for a redress scheme to be known as the New Homes Ombudsman Service (NHOS) in order to resolve disputes concerning new build homes.

The NHOS, which launched on 4 October 2022, provides a free and independent service to customers, which can impartially assess and adjudicate on issues that have arisen that fall within the Ombudsman's scope. This includes complaints around the Reservation, Legal Completion and complaints management processes, or issues or defects that have arisen at or after occupation and which are not major defects (NHOS, 2022).

The Secretary of State has the power to approve an existing, or create a new, Code of Practice, which will set high standards of build and service quality provided by developers and give homebuyers the information they need so they know what to expect. The NHOS will take into account the code of practice when investigating and determining complaints against developers.

The NHQB published its New Homes Quality Code, together with a Developer Guidance Document, in December 2021 (New Homes Quality Board, 2021). The new code of practice for the house building industry aims to drive up the quality of new build homes and strengthen protections for customers. The Code aims to fill the gaps in current protections and ensure that every aspect of a new home purchase, from when a customer walks into a sales office, through to two years after the purchase of the home is covered. The Code:

- protects vulnerable customers, prohibits high pressure selling; requires any deposits the customer pays to their builder to be protected
- requires the developer to provide all relevant information about the home during the sales process – including its tenure and any future management or service charges – that allows them to make an informed decision about their purchase

- sets out requirements for a fair reservation agreement, including a "cooling off" period and sales contract requirements
- allows customers to have a professional carry out a pre-completion inspection of their home on their behalf
- specifies that a home must be "complete", preventing builders paying customers to move into an incomplete new home early
- crucially, to address the biggest gap in the existing arrangements, the Code requires builders to have an effective after care service in place to deal with any issues or "snagging" problems customers have with their new home; together with a robust complaints process that responds to customer's concerns in a timely manner and to their satisfaction, keeping them informed throughout. If a customer is not satisfied with how any complaint they have made has been dealt with, they can refer their complaint to the NHOS.

6.9.2   *Housing Ombudsman*

Section 160 of the BSA enables social housing complainants to escalate a complaint directly to the Housing Ombudsman service, once they have completed their landlord's complaints process, thereby increasing the speed of redress.

This was achieved, with effect from 1 October 2022, by removing the existing requirement ('the democratic filter') for social housing residents wishing to escalate their complaint to the Housing Ombudsman to do this via a "designated person" that is, an MP, Councillor or recognised tenant panel or wait eight weeks after the end of their landlords' complaints process.

6.10   Construction products

The BSA introduced a freestanding cause of action against construction product manufacturers which cannot be excluded by contract. New requirements for products that are "safety critical", where their failure could cause death or serious injury to people, are to be introduced. The NRCP will become fully operational once secondary legislation has been approved by Parliament.

6.10.1   *A new construction products regime*

Sections 147 to 151 of the BSA, on 28 June 2022, introduced a freestanding cause of action against construction product manufacturers which cannot be excluded by contract. The new cause of action is available to persons with a legal or equitable interest in a dwelling which is unfit for habitation. The manufacturer of a construction product used in the dwelling will be liable to pay damages in such a case if unfitness for habitation has been caused by one of the following failings:

- The product fails to comply with a statutory requirement.
- The product is inherently defective; or
- A misleading statement has been made in relation to the product.

Liability in relation to misleading statements also applies to anyone who "markets or supplies" a construction product. Recoverable losses include damage to property and economic loss.

6.10.2 *"Safety critical" products*

New requirements for products that are "safety critical", where their failure could cause death or serious injury to people, are to be introduced. Manufacturers of these products will be required to declare their performance, put in place factory production controls to ensure that products consistently perform in line with this declaration and correct, withdraw and recall products that don't comply or that present a risk.

6.10.3 *National Regulator for Construction Products*

In January 2021, the government announced that the Office for Product Safety and Standards (OPSS) would take on responsibility for the national regulation of construction products. The intention is that the NRCP will become fully operational once secondary legislation has been approved by Parliament.

The NRCP will encourage good practice, enforce the law and educate the industry. The OPSS, in its role as the NRCP, will act on behalf of and be funded by the Department for Levelling Up, Housing and Communities (OPSS, 2022). Once legislation is in place, OPSS will:

- provide vital market surveillance and oversight, including maintaining a national complaints system and supporting local Trading Standards so that safety concerns can be spotted and dealt with quickly
- lead and coordinate the enforcement of the improved construction product regulations, including removing products that pose a safety risk from the market
- provide advice and support to the industry to improve compliance and provide technical advice to the government
- carry out or commission its own product testing to investigate non-compliance
- establish a robust and coherent approach with the BSR and Trading Standards to drive change across the sector

The NRCP will work with the industry to help them prepare to comply with the regulatory changes.

References

Statutes

Building Act 1984
Building Safety Act 2022

Secondary legislation

Regulatory Reform (Fire Safety) Order 2005
The Building (Approved Inspectors etc) Regulations 2010
The Building Regulations 2010
Town and Country Planning (Development Management Procedure and Section 62A Applications) (England) (Amendment) Order 2021

Case

Murphy v Brentwood District Council [1991] UKHL 2

Websites

BSI (2022) Digital management of fire safety information – Design, construction, handover, asset management and emergency response. Code of practice (BS 8644-1:2022), [online] Available from: https://knowledge.bsigroup.com/products/digital-management-of-fire-safety-information-design-construction-handover-asset-management-and-emergency-response-code-of-practice/standard (Accessed 6 September 2022).

DLUHC (2022) Guidance: The Building Safety Act, [online] Available from: https://www.gov.uk/guidance/the-building-safety-act (Accessed 31 October 2022).

HSE (2022a) Building Safety Regulator, [online] Available from: https://www.hse.gov.uk/building-safety/regulator.htm (Accessed 31 October 2022).

HSE (2022b) The Building Advisory Committee: Inaugural meeting, [online] Available from: https://press.hse.gov.uk/2022/12/20/the-building-advisory-committee-inaugural-meeting/ (Accessed 11 January 2023).

MHCLG (2021) Outline Transition Plan for the Building Safety Bill, [online] Available from: https://www.gov.uk/government/publications/building-safety-bill-transition-plan/outline-transition-plan-for-the-building-safety-bill (Accessed 18 August 2022).

New Homes Quality Board (2021) New Homes Quality Code published, [online] Available from: https://www.nhqb.org.uk/resource/new-homes-quality-code-published.html (Accessed 23 August 2022).

NHOS (2022) About Us, [online] Available from: https://www.nhos.org.uk/about-nhos/ (Accessed 4 November 2022).

OPSS (2022) National regulation: construction products, [online] Available from: https://www.gov.uk/government/news/national-regulation-construction-products (Accessed 18 August 2022).

7   Guidance and consultations

Jennifer Charlson

7.1   Introduction

Building safety procurement and fire risk assessment and appraisal guidance have been published. In addition, the Building Regulations Advisory Committee (BRAC) has reported on "the golden thread".

To complete the new building safety regime, the Department of Levelling Up, Housing & Communities (DLUHC) has published a number of consultations. The most significant ones are detailed, in chronological order, in the consultations section. The outcome of the consultations will inform the subsequent secondary legislation which will bring the proposed changes into force.

7.2   Guidance

The published building safety procurement and fire risk assessment and appraisal guidance are detailed below. The BRAC report on "the golden thread" is signposted.

7.2.1   Procurement guidance

Collaborative procurement guidance and *The Construction Playbook* have been published.

7.2.1.1   Collaborative procurement guidance

The "Collaborative procurement guidance for design and construction to support building safety" was developed to assist the construction industry in adopting and implementing procurement practices to deliver safe, high-quality buildings. It was published by the Department for Levelling Up, Housing and Communities on 10 January 2022 (DLUHC, 2022c).

The guidance was designed to support the regulatory regime reforms, and it recommends procurement and contracting questions that should be addressed in advance of each design and construction "gateway" application. In addition, the guidance explains how a digital golden thread can integrate design, construction and operation.

DOI: 10.1201/9781003357452-7

7.2.1.2   *The Construction Playbook*

The Building Safety Act 2022 is referenced in *The Construction Playbook* cross-cutting priority "Building safety". *The Construction Playbook* (HM Government, 2022) is the Government Guidance on sourcing and contracting public work projects and programmes.

7.2.2   *Fire risk assessment and appraisal*

A Fire Risk Assessment Prioritisation Tool and PAS 9980 2022 fire risk appraisal have been published.

7.2.2.1   *Fire Risk Assessment Prioritisation Tool*

The Fire Risk Assessment Prioritisation Tool is part of the risk-based guidance package (Home Office, 2022).

The use of the Fire Risk Assessment Prioritisation Tool, together with the risk-based guidance, should be beneficial in evidencing due diligence and assist in establishing in any proceedings that obligations under the The Regulatory Reform (Fire Safety) Order 2005 (as amended by the Fire Safety Act 2021) are being met.

7.2.2.2   *PAS 9980:2022 fire risk appraisal*

PAS (Publicly Available Specification) 9980:2022 provides a methodology for the fire risk appraisal of external wall construction and cladding of existing multi-storey and multi-occupied residential buildings (bsi, 2022).

7.2.3   *Building Regulations Advisory Committee: golden thread report*

The BRAC: golden thread report provides clarity on the golden thread policy and the changes it will require of industry. It outlines the high-level golden thread requirements including the golden thread definition and principles and how digital standards will underpin implementation of the golden thread of information (BRAC, 2021).

7.3   Consultations

To complete the new building safety regime, the DLUHC published many consultations. The most significant ones are detailed, in chronological order, below. The outcome of the consultations will inform the subsequent secondary legislation, which will bring the proposed changes into force.

7.3.1   *Consultation on the Higher Risk Buildings (Descriptions and Supplementary Provisions) Regulations*

This consultation (DLUHC, 2022g) was about the proposed Higher Risk Buildings (Descriptions and Supplementary Provisions) Regulations which complete the definition of higher-risk building for the new building safety regime. It was published by DLUHC on 9 June 2022 and closed on 21 July 2022. It sought views on the following areas:

1 the overall definition of a building for the purposes of both the design and construction and occupation parts of the new more stringent building safety regime being brought forward by the Building Safety Act
2 which buildings are included and excluded in relation to the design and construction part of the new regime and the definitions of these buildings
3 which buildings are excluded in relation to the occupation part of the new regime and the definitions of these buildings
4 the method for measuring height and number of storeys

This consultation does not relate to buildings included in the leaseholder protection scheme or the building remediation funds.

The government published the outcome of this consultation on 20 December 2022 (DLUHC, 2022k).

7.3.2   Consultation on the in-occupation regime for occupied higher-risk buildings

This consultation (DLUHC, 2022b) related to the requirement to register the building, the requirement to apply for a building assessment certificate, accountable persons, the introduction of a safety case approach to managing fire and structural safety during occupation, duties to engage residents, the ongoing management of a digital golden thread of information throughout the building lifecycle and the creation of a mandatory occurrence reporting framework.

The consultation related to the proposals for occupied higher-risk buildings under Part 4 of the Building Safety Act 2022. It was published by DLUHC on 20 July 2022 and closed on 12 October 2022.

A key part of the reforms included introducing a new, more stringent regulatory regime for high-rise residential and other in scope buildings. These are known as higher-risk buildings.

The Building Safety Act 2022 defines higher-risk buildings for the new occupation regime as buildings which contain at least two residential units and are at least 18 m in height or at least 7 storeys (whichever is reached first). The government subsequently supplemented this definition in regulations.

The new, more stringent regulatory regime will place legal responsibilities on those who commission building work, participate in the design and construction process and those who are responsible for managing structural and fire safety in higher-risk buildings when they are occupied. These people will be called dutyholders during design and construction and principal accountable persons and accountable persons when the building is occupied. When building work is carried out on an existing higher-risk building (refurbishment), this may involve both dutyholders and a principal accountable person and accountable person(s), as many buildings will remain occupied during the refurbishment.

The consultation, in 12 sections, covers policy proposals for the in-occupation phase for buildings in scope of the new, more stringent regime:

1 Registration
2 Certification
3 Accountable person(s) and the principal accountable person
4 Safety case approach
5 Mandatory occurrence reporting
6 Residents' voice and duties on residents
7 Golden thread contents
8 How the golden thread should be managed and stored
9 Duties on the accountable person(s) and the principal accountable person to share information
10 Appeals
11 Enforcement
12 Key building information

7.3.3   *Consultation on implementing the new building control regime for higher-risk buildings and wider changes to the building regulations for all buildings*

This consultation (DLUCH, 2022a) was on proposed changes to building regulations in England under Part 3 of the Building Safety Act 2022. The consultation sought views on policy proposals for legislation intended to create the building control procedure for higher-risk buildings, as well as wider changes proposed to improve the building control system overall. It was published by DLUHC on 20 July 2022 and closed on 12 October 2022.

This consultation, which was divided into 12 sections, related only to the design and construction of buildings and not to occupation requirements in higher-risk buildings:

1 New dutyholder and competence requirements on all building work and additional duties for those working on higher-risk buildings. These new roles and requirements aim to ensure a stronger focus on compliance with the regulations
2 A series of robust hard stops ("gateway points") to strengthen regulatory oversight before a higher-risk building is occupied
3 The approach to Regulator's notices to support building projects which comprise both higher-risk building work and non-higher-risk building work
4 Additional requirements for building work carried out in existing higher-risk building work e.g. refurbishments
5 Stronger change control during the construction of higher-risk buildings
6 The process of certifying building work that has been carried out without building regulations approval (regularisation)

7 Establishing better record keeping and management in higher-risk buildings (golden thread of information)

8 A mandatory occurrence reporting system in higher-risk buildings

9 More rigorous enforcement powers for building work in all buildings to focus incentives on the creation of reliably safe buildings from the outset and the approach taken to the review and appeal of building control decisions

10 Wider changes to the building regulations to align the existing system with the new system

11 The transitional provisions for changing to the new higher-risk building regime

12 Equalities assessment

In addition, the government aimed to ensure building regulations are fit for purpose across the built environment and, where appropriate, propose to apply the new approaches in the Building Safety Act 2022 to all building work, not just those in scope of the new regulatory regime for high-rise residential buildings.

7.3.4 *Residents' voice*

This consultation was on implementing the new regime for occupied higher-risk buildings related to residents' voice. It was published by DLUHC on 20 July 2022 and closed on 12 October 2022.

The proposals set out the detail of how secondary legislation under the residents' voice sections (89, 91 to 94 and 96) of the Building Safety Act 2022 will operate. The residents' voice consultation areas were as follows:

- Providing residents with building safety information – All residents will be kept informed about the safety of their building and will receive building safety information. They will also be able to request further information from the accountable person who is responsible for the part of the building which they live in.
- The residents' engagement strategy – The principal accountable person must establish a residents' engagement strategy, which promotes the participation of all residents in decisions about their building's safety and sets out how and when residents will be consulted.
- Complaints – The principal accountable person must establish and operate a system for the investigation of relevant complaints. Where a complainant believes their safety concerns have not been adequately resolved, they will have the right to escalate their complaint to the Building Safety Regulator (BSR).
- Contravention notices – Residents also have a role to play in keeping their buildings safe. The Building Safety Act 2022 places safety-related obligations on residents to help them to play their part. Where they fall short of their obligations, the accountable person can pursue compliance through the County Courts.

The cost of complying with requirements can be passed on to residents through the service charge (DLUHC, 2022f).

7.3.5   HSE consultation: The Building Safety (Fees and Charges) Regulations 202[3] and charging scheme

This consultation set out the BSR's proposals for the Building Safety (fees and charges) regulations and an underpinning charging scheme (DLUHC, 2022e). It was published by DLUHC on 1 August 2022 and closed on 7 October 2022.

7.3.6   HSE consultation: Building Safety operational standards rules

The BSR will be operating as part of the Health and Safety Executive (HSE) from April 2023. The consultation was published by DLUHC on 30 August 2022 and closed on 25 October 2022.

Views were sought on the proposed operational standards rules being developed for building control bodies. The scope included:

- Operational standards rules (OSRs)
- BSR monitoring arrangements including reportable data and key performance indicators (KPIs) for building control bodies
- the strategic context for building control oversight

The OSRs will apply to building control functions for buildings or works outside of the higher-risk building regime in England from April 2023. These functions are delivered by the building control regulators: local authorities and registered building control approvers.

The final OSRs are due to be published in Spring 2023 (DLUHC, 2022d).

7.3.7   Building Inspector Competence Framework (BICoF) consultation

Building control professionals and private sector building control organisations will have to register with BSR in order to perform building control work in England. Registration will open in October 2023 with the sections of the BSA related to registration coming into force in April 2024.

The Building Inspector Competence Framework (BICoF) consultation opened on 31 October 2022 and closed on 9 December 2022 (HSE, 2022). The BICoF applies to all who wish to register with the BSR as a Building Inspector, whether they work in the private or public sector. The final BICoF is due to be published in April 2023.

7.3.8   Building Safety Levy

The consultation on the Building Safety Levy (DLUHC, 2022h) set out proposals for how developers would pay to fix unsafe buildings. The consultation was launched by DLUHC on 22 November 2022 and closed on 7 February 2023.

Under the proposals drawn up by DLUHC, developers of residential buildings, regardless of their height, will have to pay the levy contribution as part of the building control process.

The consultation sought views on the delivery of the levy, including how it will work, what the rates will be, who must pay, what sanctions and enforcement will apply and who is responsible for collecting the levy.

7.3.9   *Building safety directors*

This consultation on building safety directors (DLUHC, 2022i) sets out proposals regarding the appointment of a person to directly support resident-led organisations in complying with their duties under Part 4 of the Building Safety Act 2022 to the board of directors of:

* Resident Management Companies through the proposed Resident Management Companies (Building Safety Directors) Regulations
* Right to Manage Companies through proposed amendments to the (Model Articles) (England) Regulations 2009

The consultation was launched by DLUHC on 1 December 2022 and closed on 7 February 2023.

7.3.10   *Sprinklers in care homes, removal of national classes, and staircases in residential buildings*

This consultation (DLUHC, 2022j) seeks views on options to recommend sprinklers in care homes, remove national classifications from Approved Document B and recommend a maximum height threshold for the use of one staircase in blocks of flats.

The consultation was launched by DLUHC on 23 December 2022 and closed on 17 March 2023.

References

Statutes

Building Safety Act 2022
Fire Safety Act 2021

Secondary legislation

Regulatory Reform (Fire Safety) Order 2005

Websites

BRAC (2021) Building Regulations Advisory Committee: golden thread report, [online] Available from: https://www.gov.uk/government/publications/building-regulations-advisory-committee-golden-thread-report/building-regulations-advisory-committee-golden-thread-report#golden-thread-definition (Accessed 11 January 2023).
bsi (2022) PAS 9980:2022, [online] Available from: https://www.bsigroup.com/en-GB/standards/pas-9980/ (Accessed 26 October 2022).

DLUHC (2022a) Consultation on implementing the new building control regime for higher-risk buildings and wider changes to the building regulations for all buildings, [online] Available from: https://consult.levellingup.gov.uk/building-safety/part-3-building-regulations-consultation/ (Accessed 17 August 2022).

DLUHC (2022b) Consultation on the in-occupation regime for occupied higher-risk buildings, [online] Available from: https://consult.levellingup.gov.uk/building-safety/consultation-on-the-in-occupation-regime-for-occup/ (Accessed 17 August 2022).

DLUHC (2022c) Collaborative procurement guidance for design and construction to support building safety, [online] Available from: https://www.gov.uk/government/publications/collaborative-procurement-guidance-for-design-and-construction-to-support-building-safety (Accessed 16 August 2022).

DLUHC (2022d) HSE Consultation: Building Safety Operational Standards Rules, [online] Available from: https://consult.levellingup.gov.uk/building-safety/hse-consultation-building-safety-operational-stand/ (Accessed 1 September 2022).

DLUHC (2022e) HSE Consultation: The Building Safety (Fees and Charges) Regulations 202[3] and charging scheme, [online] Available from: https://consult.levellingup.gov.uk/building-safety/the-building-safety-fees-and-charges-regulations-2/ (Accessed 1 September 2022).

DLUHC (2022f) Residents' Voice, [online] Available from: https://consult.levellingup.gov.uk/building-safety/residents-voice/?utm_source=govdelivery&utm_medium=email&utm_campaign=bsr-hse&utm_term=consultations-2&utm_content=bsr-aug-22 (Accessed 1 September 2022).

DLUHC (2022g) Consultation on the Higher Risk Buildings (Descriptions and Supplementary Provisions) Regulations, [online] Available from: https://www.gov.uk/government/consultations/consultation-on-the-higher-risk-buildings-descriptions-and-supplementary-provisions-regulations/consultation-on-the-higher-risk-buildings-descriptions-and-supplementary-provisions-regulations#:~:text=For%20the%20in%2Doccupation%20part, at%20least%20two%20residential%20units (Accessed 1 February 2022).

DLUHC (2022h) Building safety levy moves a step closer, [online] Available from: https://www.gov.uk/government/news/building-safety-levy-moves-a-step-closer?utm_source=govdelivery&utm_medium=email&utm_campaign=bsr&utm_term=levy&utm_content=bsr-29-nov-22 (Accessed 19 December 2022).

DLUHC (2022i) Building safety directors: consultation, [online] Available from: https://www.gov.uk/government/consultations/building-safety-directors-consultation?utm_source=govdelivery&utm_medium=email&utm_campaign=bsr-hse&utm_term=govt-2&utm_content=bsr-4-jan-23 (Accessed 11 January 2023).

DLUHC (2022j) Sprinklers in care homes, removal of national classes, and staircases in residential buildings, [online] Available from: https://www.gov.uk/government/consultations/sprinklers-in-care-homes-removal-of-national-classes-and-staircases-in-residential-buildings (Accessed 11 January 2023).

DLUHC (2022k) Government response to the Higher-Risk Buildings (Descriptions and Supplementary Provisions) Regulations consultation, [online] Available from: https://www.gov.uk/government/consultations/consultation-on-the-higher-risk-buildings-descriptions-and-supplementary-provisions-regulations/outcome/government-response-to-the-higher-risk-buildings-descriptions-and-supplementary-provisions-regulations-consultation?utm_source=govdelivery&utm_medium=email&utm_campaign=bsr-hse&utm_term=govt-3&utm_content=bsr-4-jan-23 (Accessed 11 January 2023).

HM Government (2022) The Construction Playbook, [online] Available from: https://assets.publishing.service.gov.uk/government/uploads/system/uploads/attachment_data/file/1102386/14.116_CO_Construction_Playbook_Web.pdf (Accessed 26 October 2022).

Home Office (2022) Fire Risk Assessment Prioritisation Tool, [online] Available from: https://bpt.homeoffice.gov.uk/ (Accessed 24 August 2022).

HSE (2022) Building inspector Competence Framework (BICoF) consultation, [online] Available from: https://consultations.hse.gov.uk/bsr/bicof-consultation/?utm_source=govdelivery&utm_medium=email&utm_campaign=bsr&utm_term=consultation&utm_content=bsr-31-oct-22 (Accessed 31 October 2022).

8   Conclusions

Jennifer Charlson and Nenpin Dimka

This chapter brings together conclusions from the previous chapters:

1   Background
2   Grenfell Tower fire
3   Remediation of existing buildings
4   Legal framework
5   Regulations
6   Regulators
7   Guidance and consultations

8.1   Background

The narrative of Chapter 1 endeavoured to establish the fires which have occurred in the UK and key factors which could have served as warning signs to prevent the extent of the disaster of the Grenfell fire. These fires had considerable lessons, which were identified following investigations in the aftermath of the events. The historical instances of a lack of prioritising safety concerns and failure to ensure compliance with regulations, including allowing the use of materials which were known to have been combustible or not fit for purpose, are unmistakable.

The potential risks stemming from the lack of coordination at the design stage have been observed with Summerland. Flaws in evacuation strategies, the application of the stay-put and its limitation have been experienced. Such as the case of the Harrow Court fire, where the stay-put policy was ineffective given compartmentalisation was compromised. The benefits of the fire brigade involvement in ensuring fire safety in tower blocks and the advantage of sprinklers in the event of a fire have been advocated.

Similarly, the knowledge of the dangers of using combustible materials and the implication to spread of fire, particularly with the well-established approach of over-cladding residential tower blocks with rain screen cladding system which incorporates cavities, were not restricted. In the case of Knowsley Heights, the consequence of the combination of new cladding, with insufficient cavity barriers, and the installation of new windows of reduced size aided the spread of fire.

DOI: 10.1201/9781003357452-8

The importance of awareness of evacuation strategies by residents and firefighters, along with and installation of sprinklers, was again identified in the incident at Lakanal House. Finally, the ambiguity of the Approved Documents (ADs) as guidance and their implication to compliance has been known.

8.2   The Grenfell Tower fire

The Grenfell Tower fire demonstrated an overall systemic failure in the UK construction industry along with a failure to learn from the historical lessons of previous fires. The tragic event at Grenfell bears several similarities to fires which have occurred in residential tower blocks.

The consequences of the nature of materials used in the refurbishment, the limited fire prevention measures in the cladding system and the installation of new components of reduced size were well understood in the event of a fire.

However, in this unique case, the voice of the residents can be considered a new lesson to be learned. The residents had tried to register safety concerns with the authorities with no success. Several of these concerns were later understood to have contributed to the extent of the disaster.

The Hackitt Review revealed deficiencies in building safety were systemic, caused by a complexity involving insufficient regulatory oversight and ineffective enforcement. To address these problems, the industry must move towards an integrated system of safety protection instead of focusing on changes in the components of a system. This has given rise to the new regulatory reform developed with a focus on high-rise residential buildings along with the creation of new duty holders and a shift towards outcome-based guidance.

The Grenfell Inquiry was a robust investigation of every aspect of the disaster. Phase 1, conducted over seven months, focused on factual narratives of the events on the night of 14th June 2017. Phase 2 of the Inquiry spanned 18 months and was concerned with the causes of these events, including how the Tower was in a condition that allowed the spread of fire identified in Phase 1.

8.3   Remediation of existing buildings

In response to the pressure to remediate existing buildings, the government has responded with a number of initiatives. The government established remediation, building safety and waking watch relief and replacement funds:

- Social Sector ACM Cladding Remediation Fund with costs estimated at £400 million
- Private Sector ACM Cladding Remediation Fund with costs estimated at £200 million
- Building Safety Fund with provision of £4.5 billion
- Waking Watch Relief Fund with provision of £35 million
- Waking Watch Replacement Fund with provision of £27 million

In February 2021, the government announced a five-point plan to bring an end to unsafe cladding. In July 2021, the Independent Expert Statement on Building Safety in medium and lower rise blocks of flats was published with the government responding that it would support and act on their five recommendations.

The government, in January 2022, announced that it had reset its approach to building safety with a new plan to protect leaseholders and make developers and companies pay to fix the cladding crisis. The Secretary of State wrote to the residential property developer industry asking them to agree to make financial contributions, fund and undertake all necessary remediation of buildings and provide comprehensive information on some buildings.

The government withdrew the Consolidated Advice Note – interim guidance which had been wrongly interpreted by the industry as requiring remediation of all cladding irrespective of building height.

The 4% Residential Property Developer Tax came into force on 1 April 2022. Also, in April 2022, the government announced the potential extension of the scope of the Building Safety Levy to all residential and mixed use buildings.

In May 2022, the government published its response to the Levelling Up, Housing and Communities Select Committee's reports, published in April 2021 and March 2022, following its inquiries into cladding remediation and building safety remediation and funding in England.

The Secretary of State, in June 2022, wrote to the freeholders, building landlords and managing agents making it clear that building owners must take responsibility for remediating unsafe buildings and that any parties who continue to seek to recover costs from leaseholders in relation to historic defects will be committing a criminal offence.

The Building Safety Act (BSA) 2022 provisions relating to the remediation of existing fire safety defects came into force in June 2022. Up to July 2022, 48 of the UK's major housebuilders had signed up to the government's Building Safety Pledge, agreeing to pay to fix buildings over 11 m with life critical fire safety defects they developed or refurbished in the last 30 years. The September 2022 Building Safety Programme data was the 59th monthly data release.

In 2022, *Martlet v Mulalley* was the first substantive decision on fire safety since Grenfell. A housing association won a landmark cladding claim, just over five years after the Grenfell Tower fire, against a building contractor on external wall systems. In the subsequent *St James's Oncology SPC v Lendlease Construction* case, the judge found against the contractor because the constructed installation, within the Plantroom and the electrical substation, was not built to the designed fire strategy.

In October 2022, the Recovery Strategy Unit took the first step in legal action against a freeholder who had not committed to remediating a tower's fire safety defects.

8.4   Legal framework

The BSA , which received Royal Assent on 28 April 2022, contains provisions intended to secure the safety of people in or about buildings and to improve the standard of buildings. Many of the detailed provisions were to be implemented, in the two years following Royal Assent, through a programme of secondary legislation.

The BSA protects leaseholders, residents of higher-risk buildings and home-owners. Accountable persons will need to demonstrate that they have effective, proportionate measures in place to manage building risks in the higher-risk buildings for which they are responsible. Those who do not meet their obligations may face criminal charges. Building owners and landlords will need to contribute to the costs of fixing their own buildings.

The BSA will create a framework for the design, construction and management of safer, high-quality homes. There will be a new developer tax and a levy on developers. New rights to redress will ensure those responsible for contributing to the building safety crisis will be liable for costs to rectify their mistakes.

On 28 June 2022, the following provisions of the BSA came into force:

- New financial protections for leaseholders in buildings above 11 m or 5 storeys with historical safety defects
- Limitation periods in which a potential claimant can bring a claim under the Defective Premises Act 1972 amended from six years from completion of a dwelling, to either
  - a 30-year limitation period for dwellings completed before 28 June 2022 or
  - 15 years for dwellings to be completed after 28 June 2022
- A new prospective right of action against any person who "takes on work in relation to any part" of a dwelling meaning that claims may now be brought in respect of any refurbishment or remedial works completed on an existing building subject to the new 15-year limitation period
- Building liability, remediation and remediation contribution orders
- A damages claim can be brought against a manufacturer of construction products whose breaches of the Construction Products Regulations 1991 cause a building or dwelling to become unfit for habitation
- Strengthening the powers that the Architects Registration Board has under the Architects Act 1997

With effect from 28 July 2022, the requirements relating to insurance for Approved Inspectors were removed from the Building Act 1984.

The intention was that the bulk of the new provisions would be brought into force within 12 to 18 months of Royal Assent.

New restrictions on the combustibility of materials contained within external walls of "relevant buildings" in England came into force on 21 December 2018. The Combustible Materials Ban, which was introduced in England in 2018 following the Grenfell Tower Fire, was amended with effect from 1 December 2022.

The Regulatory Reform (Fire Safety) Order 2005 was, on 16 May 2022, amended to make clear it applies to the structure, external walls (including cladding and balconies) and individual flat entrance doors between domestic premises and the common parts. The Fire Safety (England) Regulations 2022 came into force on 23 January 2023.

8.5   Regulations

The historical overview in this chapter serves to create links between the Legislature, the Regulations and the ADs. The Building Act 1984 imposes a set of requirements governing the design and construction of buildings to ensure the health, safety and welfare of people in and around buildings. The Building Regulations 2010 establish minimum requirements and basic performance standards. The ADs support the Building Regulations by providing generic guidance.

Following the ADs is considered evidence of compliance with the Building Regulations. However, there are no obligations to adopt the particular solutions contained in them, and other approaches may be utilised so far as performance standards are attained. The ADs are subject to amendments in order to meet the growing demand for better, safer, accessible structures and reduced environmental damage as well when found to be deficient.

The fire at Grenfell highlighted limitations in the guidance provided by the Approved Document B: Fire Safety which has subsequently been amended. A ban on combustible cladding was introduced to the Building Regulations on 21st December 2018. It prohibits the use of combustible materials on the external walls of high-rise buildings.

There have been extensive changes made to both volumes of Approved Document B, including the updating of the document format and the simplifying of its language. As a result, most sections have been revised (including numbering) in the 2020 amendments.

The changes in the 2022 amendment, which took effect on 1 December 2022 for use in England and focused on the fire safety provisions, included a ban of combustible materials in and on the external walls of buildings, the new recommendation for secure information boxes in blocks of flats with storeys over 11m, evacuation alert systems and clarification of further diagrams.

8.6   Regulators

The Building Safety Regulator (BSR) is due to become operational in April 2023. The BSR has three main functions:

1 Overseeing the safety and performance system for all buildings
2 Assisting and encouraging the improvement of competence in the built environment industry and among building control professionals
3 Leading implementation of the new, more stringent regulatory regime for higher-risk buildings

The BSR has a duty to establish and maintain three committees: Residents' Panel, Industry Competence Committee and Building Advisory Committee.

New duties for "higher-risk buildings" during the occupation phase of a building have been introduced. The higher-risk buildings in scope are over 18 m or 7 or more storeys and contain at least 2 residential units. The design and construction phases of hospitals and care homes are also within scope. Over time, however, the scope is likely to expand to include other buildings where people sleep and buildings of lower height.

All occupied higher-risk buildings will have one clearly identifiable accountable person and must be registered with the BSR by October 2023. It is a criminal offence if a building is occupied but not registered after this date.

The BSR must establish and maintain a register of building inspectors and building control approvers and prepare and publish their code of conduct and professional conduct rules. The BSR may inspect, investigate, report and discipline these professionals.

The BSR will regulate developments through a series of three gateways. Permission from the BSR will be required before a development can proceed through each gateway. Gateway 1, which governs the planning stage, is already in force. From October 2023, developers will also have to pass through gateway 2 prior to the start of building work and gateway 3 upon the works' completion.

Occupational phase building safety duties are shared between dutyholders. The Accountable Person will need to apply for a Building Assessment Certificate. The BSA creates new imprisonable criminal offences to ensure those responsible for the safety of high-rise residential buildings comply with their responsibilities.

The New Homes Ombudsman Service, launched on 4 October 2022, aims to resolve disputes concerning new build homes. With effect from 1 October 2022, social housing complainants can escalate a complaint directly to the Housing Ombudsman service once they have completed their landlord's complaints process.

The BSA, on 28 June 2022, introduced a freestanding cause of action against construction product manufacturers which cannot be excluded by contract. New requirements for products that are "safety critical", where their failure could cause death or serious injury to people, are to be introduced. The National Regulator for Construction Products will become fully operational once secondary legislation has been approved by Parliament.

8.7 Guidance and consultations

The "Collaborative procurement guidance for design and construction to support building safety" was developed to assist the construction industry in adopting and implementing procurement practices to deliver safe, high-quality buildings. *The Construction Playbook* identifies "Building safety" as a cross-cutting priority.

The Fire Risk Assessment Prioritisation Tool is part of the risk-based guidance package. PAS 9980:2022 provides a methodology for the fire risk appraisal of external wall construction and cladding of existing multi-storey and multi-occupied residential buildings.

The Building Regulations Advisory Committee: golden thread report provides clarity on the golden thread policy and the changes it will require of industry.

To complete the new building safety regime, the Department of Levelling Up, Housing & Communities has published many consultations. The outcome of the consultations will inform the subsequent secondary legislation which will bring the proposed changes into force.

Index

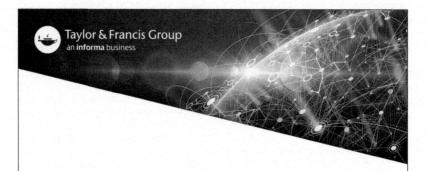